AROMA THERAPY

Nerys Purchon

Styling by Louise Owens

Photography by Quentin Bacon

Grange
BOOKS

Published by Grange Books
An Imprint of Grange Books PLC
The Grange
Grange Yard
London SE1 3AG

Produced by Hodder Headline Australia Pty Limited,
(A member of the Hodder Headline Group)
10-16 South Street, Rydalmere NSW 2116, Australia

This edition published in 1995

ISBN 1 85627 684 8

Editor: Jan Castorina
Designer: Melanie Feddersen
Editorial Assistant: Ella Martin
Herb Photography: Ivy Hansen
Consultant: Paul Callinan

Printed in Australia by Mc Pherson's Printing Group, Melbourne

CONTENTS

AROMATHERAPY

Some of the happiest years of my life were spent on a small farm called 'Rivendell' where Prakash (my husband) and I, together with family and friends, had a small company making natural, herbal and cruelty-free cosmetics. I began to appreciate the heavily perfumed air as the early morning sun warmed the herbs and released their perfumes; began to notice that on a cold, wet day there was very little of the perfume released even if some of the leaves became crushed; I began to find an attraction to a certain plant and then to discover that that plant was the one I needed most at that time.

Since that time I have used the oils every day in many different ways and each day feel that I gain a greater depth of love and understanding of these magical essences. When I rub a leaf or petal, I feel as excited as Aladdin was when he rubbed the magic lamp and released the genie. My genie is the oil which, when released, will perform all sorts of wonderful magic for me. The contents of this book are largely the result of the things I have learnt during and since this time.

You will feel enriched when you, your family and friends are using the gifts of the earth to improve your lives. To see the raw materials transformed into beautiful and richly scented unguents, perfumes, sachets, room fresheners and other lovely things is a very special experience.

Our sense of smell is the most evocative sense we possess, as it is connected to the part of the brain responsible for memory. Which of us is not transported back to other places and other days by a sudden waft of fragrant perfume?

I sincerely hope that you will find this book inspirational. The recipes in this book are not at all difficult. They don't take long to make and most of them are quite inexpensive. The biggest cost will be the purchase of the oils. Consider how much you spend in a year on skin and hair-care items, perfumes, household cleaning and disinfectant products, garden and personal insect sprays and repellents, medicinal items and you will realise that your initial outlay is small by comparison.

I always carry a little tin box of emergency oils. It's astonishing how often I am called upon to use them and how appreciated they are. Learn to love the oils and keep them close to you.

Derys Purchon

OPPOSITE: *Credit: Flowers from Lisa Milasas.*

AROMATICS AND ESSENTIAL OILS

The earliest records of the use of aromatics are of their religious significance, being used as oils for anointing, incense for burning and waters for washing both priests and altars; two of the gifts brought to Jesus by the wise men were the exquisitely perfumed resins frankincense and myrrh. Three thousand years ago aromatics were being used in China, India and Egypt and were a large part of their trade; ships sailed through perilous waters carrying their precious and luxurious cargoes among which were spices, scented woods, gums, resins and camphor.

There is little if any mention of the therapeutic properties of essential oils until the end of the last century BC when the Greek physician Marestheus is credited with having been for healing but, were probably being used long before this time.

Many books suggest that the main use (apart from in religious ceremonies) of the crudely extracted oils from aromatic botanicals was to mask and disguise the smells of dirty places and people. I feel that this is doing a disservice to the intelligence of the people who used the herbs and oils. If we examine the biblical references we discover that the herbs and oils mentioned all had strongly therapeutic actions — surely not an accident.

The medieval Arabian physician Avicenna is credited with the discovery of the distillation of essential oils from plants. Essential oils are volatile compounds that occur naturally in plants. In some cases the oil is excreted, giving the plant a characteristic scent which attracts insects; in others the oil isn't apparent unless the plant is crushed or dried (the root of valerian being an example). Some oils are not apparent until incisions are made in the bark to release the resin or gum of the plant and many of these have no perfume until they are dried.

Essential oils have been variously described as the life force or essence of plants. The essential oil is contained in miniscule quantities in most plants; consequently many of the oils are very expensive.

The essence or essential oil of plants is found in leaves (such as eucalyptus), petals (rose), bark (sandalwood), resins (myrrh), roots (calamus), rind (citrus fruits) and seeds (caraway).

The word oil causes some confusion as people tend to think of these essences as being the same as olive, safflower and other fixed oils. Essential oils are non-oily and, unlike the fixed oils, they evaporate when exposed to air.

The term 'aromatherapy' was first used in the 1920s by René Maurice Gattefosse, a French chemist who used the term to describe 'a therapy using aromatics'. One account states that Gattefosse burnt his hand and thrust it into the nearest liquid to quell the pain; the liquid happened to be a tub of lavender oil which not only eased the pain but caused the burn to heal very quickly.

The word aromatherapy implies that the cure or treatment lies in the inhalation of the aroma (perfume) of the plant extract being used. Whilst this is true, it is only part of the story. These precious essences are composed of molecules small enough to penetrate the skin and enter the blood stream and so may be employed in many ways.

The essential oils can be:

- incorporated with carrier oils to make massage oils
- added to water to be used as fomentations and compresses
- added in minute quantities to baths
- added to alcohol to make toilet waters and perfumes
- incorporated with any carrier to make insect repellents
- incorporated in cosmetic creams, and healing ointments
- used in shampoos, conditioners and hair tonics
- used to strengthen the perfume of potpourris
- used to add antibacterial qualities to room freshener sprays
- used in preparations for pets, to heal skin conditions and repel fleas
- added to floor and furniture cleaners

Cautions

Some essences are toxic and should only be used internally on the advice of a qualified aromatherapist or naturopath.

All essential oils should be kept well out of the reach of children as most would prove lethal if drunk — even in small quantities.

It is essential that you read the information provided in 'A–Z of Oils' (see page 76), carefully noting the cautions, as some oils are toxic in large quantities and others must be avoided during pregnancy.

Most of the oils should be combined with a carrier (or base) oil such as olive or sweet almond oil before using externally as they are too strong to use alone. The total amount of all essential oils (either singly or combined with other ingredients) should never exceed 3% of the total amount and some oils should be used in far smaller amounts. See 'Blending and Storing Oils', on page 14.

It's imperative to use only the best essential oils available; synthetics and compounded oils don't have the healing properties of the real thing and could be dangerous if taken internally. Many oils are labelled 'fragrant oil', 'compounded oil', 'perfume oil'. These descriptions mean that the oil is either synthetic or blended with either paraffin oil or a carrier oil. Check with the retailer that the oil labelled '100% pure, natural, essential oil' is in fact what it purports to be; if in doubt, wait until you find a reliable source. Another check is cost: if oils such as rose, jasmine or neroli (to mention but a few) are roughly the same price as the more common lavender, rosemary and peppermint, then they are almost certainly not the real thing.

EQUIPMENT

I have a special cupboard in which I store all my ingredients and equipment. A strong cardboard box will do just as well if you haven't many things to store.

It's wise to set aside special equipment for making the recipes, as the powerfully perfumed essential oils are absorbed into wooden spoons and utensils and ruin food with their strong perfumes. Beeswax is very difficult to clean off pans and dishes so it's best to save those pans for recipes containing beeswax.

If you are going to make very small quantities of creams and lotions you can make them in the jar in which they will be stored.

Search the second-hand shops or buy:
- Big and little pans (not aluminium)
- Wooden spoons, teaspoons, tablespoons
- Coarse, medium and fine sieves
- 1 or 2 funnels
- Rubber spatulas
- Scissors
- Large and small sharp knives
- 2 or 3 measuring jugs
- 2 or 3 mixing bowls
- Set of measuring cups
- Mortar and pestle or electric coffee grinder
- Screw-top jars and bottles, different sizes
- Tea towels
- Double boiler (not aluminium)
- Roasting pan or electric frypan
- Coffee filter papers
- Scales (dieters scales are relatively inexpensive and can be purchased from most variety stores and pharmacies)
- Preserves/jam making, sugar or laboratory thermometer (2 if possible)
- Plastic measure (25ml/about 1fl oz)
- Eye droppers
- Cheesecloth for making little bags and for fine straining
- Labels for jars
- Waterproof marking pen, fine tip
- Electric blender or food processor or whisk

To make many of the recipes in this book you will need a double boiler which is simply a pan in a pan. The mixture is in the top pan and the water in the bottom pan. The mixture is protected from burning by having no contact with direct heat and the temperature is easier to control.

An electric frypan half full of water to hold bowls or jars is an ideal arrangement as it frees you from dependency on a stove and you could use the laundry as your laboratory.

A deep roasting pan half filled with water and used on the stove is an alternative or a heatproof bowl which fits snugly into a saucepan.

Small amounts of the mixture may be made in a little jar that the preparation will be stored in, by standing the jar in warm water in a small shallow pan.

Make sure that all equipment is scrupulously clean before you begin. This is important, as the cleaner your equipment and storage containers, the longer your aromatic products will keep fresh and uncontaminated.

All glass containers should be washed in soapy water, rinsed, and dried at the bottom of an oven which is set on low. Alternatively the bottles or jars can be boiled in water for 20 minutes — place a folded cloth in the bottom of the pan.

Plastics may be sterilised by soaking in water to which sodium metabisulphite (obtainable from pharmacies) has been added.

OPPOSITE: Credits: Scales, porcelain dishes and funnel from The Bay Tree. Bread board from Tully's Northside Timber Stripping and Finishing. Flowers from Lisa Milasas.

BEESWAX

Beeswax can be bought from a pharmacy (expensive), health food store or from a beekeeper (much cheaper). Beeswax from a beekeeper is likely to be full of bits and pieces such as bees legs and wings, flower scraps etc. and will need cleansing before use.

Cleansing Beeswax

Place the beeswax in a large old pan, cover with water and heat very slowly until the wax has melted. Allow to cool.

Lift the wax off the surface of the water and scrape away the layer of dark material which will have gathered underneath. Repeat if necessary.

Beeswax Cubes

The reason for making beeswax cubes is to create manageable amounts of wax, as it is very difficult to cut small pieces from a large block. In many books, the recipes for ointments etc., require a tablespoon or teaspoon of grated beeswax — if you've ever tried to measure a spoon of grated wax, you would know how difficult it is to do this accurately, as there is rarely any suggestion as to whether the wax should be finely or coarsely grated, loosely or tightly packed.

The following method ensures that a large number of cubes of the same weight can be made in one session. Any other hard substance, such as emulsifying wax, may be treated in this way, making the process much quicker when you want to make a batch of cream or ointment.

Melt the cleansed wax (very gently or it might burn) and pour it into greased ice cube trays to set. Weigh the resulting cubes (usually about 12–15g ($\frac{1}{3}$–$\frac{1}{2}$oz) each depending on the ice cube tray). Store in an insect-proof container as there is a moth which adores beeswax. Label the container with the average cube weight.

ESSENCES

Essential oils are often called essences but for the purpose of this book an essence is a mixture of 15ml ($\frac{1}{2}$fl oz) essential oil and 1 cup (250ml/ 8fl oz) high proof vodka. This is a 6% solution.

INHALATIONS

To make an inhalation you need essential oils, a heatproof bowl, boiling water and 2 large towels.

Place the bowl on a folded towel on the table; make sure the bowl is very stable and won't slip. Half fill the bowl with boiling water, sit on a chair close to the table, with a towel draped over your shoulders. Sprinkle the water with all the essential oils listed (up to 6 drops). Immediately cover your head, shoulders and the bowl with the towel, and breath in the medicated steam for 5–10 minutes.

Don't go out of doors for some time after having an inhalation as your mucous membranes will be sensitive and cold air could have an adverse effect.

Caution

If you are giving an inhalation to a very young or very old person, you must be very careful to avoid accidents with the boiling water. Stay with the patient the whole time and hold the bowl firmly.

If the patient is a baby it's better to pour boiling water in the washbasin in the bathroom and shut the door. Sprinkle 1–4 drops of essential oil (depending on the age of the baby) on the surface of the water and let the baby inhale the steam coming from the basin. This is also a good system to use for a frail, very sick or aged person.

FOMENTATIONS

Fomentations are ways of applying heat, cold, stimulation, moisture or the healing properties of various agents to areas of the body.

As a general rule a cold compress is used for soothing and withdrawing heat from an area and reducing swelling. Hot poultices ease pain, relax spasms, draw pus and relieve congestion.

If the fomentation or compress is to be used on the face it should never be applied too hot or too cold to areas where it could break the tiny capillaries. To make fomentations:

1. Soak a piece of soft cloth in very hot water then add the chosen essential oils.
2. Wring out the excess liquid and test the cloth on your wrist for temperature.
3. Apply as hot as can be comfortably borne. Cover if possible to keep the heat in.
4. Repeat often for 2 hours or until relief is obtained.

Compresses are made in the same way as a fomentation but very cold liquid is used instead of hot. The compress needs to be changed as soon as it becomes warm.

MAKING OINTMENTS

Ointments, salves or unguents as they are sometimes called, are usually a water-in-oil emulsion combined with herbs or essential oils and used for healing. An emulsion is a mixture of oil and water which, when combined, does not separate.

In this emulsion the oil is the main ingredient and has water packed into it in microscopically small droplets. This type of emulsion forms a cream or lotion which feels oily when first applied to the skin. Most creams containing beeswax, cocoa butter and coconut oil are water in oil emulsions and have a greasy feel which largely disperses as the cream is massaged into the skin.

I'm sure that you, like me, will derive a great deal of pleasure from making ointments. I get a strong feeling of a connection with the herbalists and witches of centuries ago who made these preparations in much the same way as I describe.

The tricky part of ointment making is knowing when to pour it into the jar. If you pour too soon the emulsion might break; too late and the mixture won't pour.

Water-in-Oil Emulsion

1. Melt hard waxes until liquid but not overheated.
2. Add the softer ingredients such as lanolin and then dissolve.
3. Add oils very slowly, stopping if the wax begins to solidify, and heat only enough to keep the mixture liquid.
4. Slowly trickle in the warmed water, stirring constantly and stopping if the mixture begins to solidify. Heat slightly until all is once again liquid.
5. Add tinctures and essential oils when the mixture is below 45–48°C (113–118°F). Mix in thoroughly and, when all is a homogenous mass, pour into sterilised jars and seal immediately.

Basic Method

The following recipe makes 2 x 50g (1²⁄₃oz) jars but it's much easier to make a larger quantity. Jars of ointment are never wasted as they will keep for months in the refrigerator and make excellent gifts.

½ cube (7g/¼oz) beeswax
40g (1¹⁄₃oz) lanolin
40ml (1¹⁄₃fl oz) olive, safflower or
grape seed oil (see page 91)
80 drops essential oil

Melt the beeswax in a small pan. Add the lanolin and melt. Add the oil slowly while stirring. Take the pan off the heat and cool slightly to 45–48°C (113–118°F).

Add the essential oil. Stir until the mixture thickens slightly. Pot at once.

Straining and Filtering

To ensure the longest possible life for liquid preparations they should be thoroughly strained. Coffee filter papers are useful for fine straining of recipes where a sparkling liquid is desirable.

EXTRACTION

DISTILLATION

The most widely used commercial method of extracting essential oil is by distillation, where direct contact with either steam, boiling water (or both) is used. The evaporated oil and steam is then passed in coils through a container of cold water and a container separates the oil.

SOLVENT EXTRACTION

Another method employed by the perfume industry is the solvent method which uses a spirit solvent, often petroleum ether, to dissolve the oil in the plant. The solvent is evaporated off leaving a hard, heavily perfumed natural wax substance called a concrete. The wax is then separated from the essence and the resulting liquid is called an absolute which is the most concentrated perfume available. This method produces a purer perfume than distillation but it needs individual and technological expertise, is more expensive and very difficult to do at home.

ENFLEURAGE

A time-honoured method of recovering essential oil from petals which retain their perfume for some time after collection (such as tuberose, rose and jasmine) is called 'enfleurage'. This method, though time consuming, is easy to do at home:

1. Spread a thin layer of pure lard or hardened vegetable fat (not margarine) on a glass or enamel sheet.
2. Press a single layer of heavily perfumed fresh flower petals onto the fat. Lay another sheet of glass on top. Leave for 24 hours. Pick the petals off the fat and replace with more petals.
3. Repeat the above process for 7–21 days or until the perfume is as strong as you desire.
4. Pick off the petals and scrape the fat into a small bowl. Cover the bowl and place it into a pan of hot water to melt the fat . Don't overheat.
5. Add a few drops of a fixative oil such as sandalwood, pour the melted fat into little pots and put lids on at once.

The resulting scented fat is called a sachet or cream perfume and may be used in the same way as liquid perfume. If you prefer a liquid cologne/toilet water, you can stop the above after stage 3 and proceed as follows:

4. Pick off the petals and either scrape the fat into a jar or if hard, chop into walnut-sized pieces.
5. Cover with vodka or other high proof alcohol which has little or no smell.
6. Cover with a leakproof lid and store in a dark place for 3–4 weeks, shaking daily.
7. Strain or skim the fat from the alcohol, add a few drops of one of the fixative oils to the alcohol and pour into small, well-stoppered bottles. Now you have genuine home-made cologne.

If, after removing the fat (stage 7), the alcohol is evaporated away in a double boiler over a very gentle heat, you will be left with pure essential oil. The amount however will be miniscule and there is always a danger of overheating and evaporating the oil along with the alcohol.

MACERATION

If you have masses of perfumed petals you can use the following method to make a deliciously scented oil. The petals don't have to be from the same type of flower, as a mixed perfume blend can be very pleasant. The method is very simple, but a steady, very gentle source of heat is essential. I put the jar on the top of the refrigerator, towards the back where the rising heat from the coils remains gentle and constant.

1. Quarter fill a jar with cotton wool balls. Cover them with an unscented oil such as sweet almond or grape seed.
2. Pack the jar with fresh, slightly crushed, heavily scented petals.
3. Cover with a tightly fitting lid and leave in a constantly warm place for 2 days.
4. Take out the petals and replace with fresh ones. Repeat these procedures for up to a month.
5. Squeeze the cotton balls to extract as much perfumed oil as possible.

OPPOSITE: *Credits: Jar from Tully's Northside Timber Stripping and Finishing. Flowers from Lisa Milasas.*

EXPRESSION

The oil in citrus plants is contained in glands in the outer skin. Before machines were invented, the skins of the citrus were squeezed by hand until the glands burst, the droplets were collected in sponges which were then squeezed to collect the oil in containers.

This squeezing method can be used at home. Collect the droplets with either a small cosmetic sponge or cotton wool balls, or fold a small piece of cheesecloth. If the amount of oil collected is too small to squeeze out, the sponge or ball can be dropped into either a little vodka or almond oil, left overnight and then squeezed out leaving the essential oil in the carrier oil or alcohol.

This is a good way of making full use of skins which would otherwise be wasted.

BLENDING AND STORING OILS

BLENDING AND DILUTING THE OILS

For easy measuring and for safety's sake, I would strongly advise you to buy accurate measures.

The total amount of all essential oils used (either singly or combined with other essential oils) in a blend should never exceed 3% of the total and some oils are used in smaller amounts.

A pharmacist will usually be able to supply, or tell you where to obtain, a dropper which is marked in amounts up to 1ml and glass or plastic (not as good) beakers or hypodermic syringes which will measure amounts from 1ml upwards.

A set of metric measuring spoons is more accurate than regular household spoons, but still not as good as those made to pharmaceutical or laboratory standards. A guide for measures is:

18–20 drops = 1ml = 1 marked dropper
90–100 drops = 5ml = 1 metric teaspoon

In any sized bottle the main content will be a carrier or base, such as oil, vinegar or alcohol, in which to dilute the essential oils.

STORING THE OILS

Correct storage of your essential oils is very important. The oils should be kept, tightly capped, in dark bottles away from heat and light as these are spoilers. Another major spoiler is air. Oil bottles should be kept as full as possible. When the level of oil in a bottle has dropped to half, the oil should be decanted into a smaller bottle. While this seems like a lot of work it is wise to protect your quite considerable investment.

The length of life of essential oils is arguable. Different oils have different lengths of life and storage is a major factor. A rough estimate would be 2 years but I have oils older than this which are still good.

BLENDING GUIDE

This list gives the amount of essential oils to use in a blend. Use with the
Blending Chart (below) as a guide for specific bottle sizes.

Massage oils	2–2.5%
Face oils	1–1.5%
Fomentations and Compresses	10 drops – 100ml (3½fl oz)
Ointments	3%
Creams and lotions	1–1.5%
Baths	10 drops maximum. See Baths (page 33) for instructions.
Insect repellent rubs	2–2.5%
Room sprays, all types	1 teaspoon in 50ml (1⅔fl oz) alcohol. Dissolve and then add 250ml (8fl oz) purified water
Shampoos and conditioners	1–1.5ml
Pomander	See method on page 50
Pet shampoo	1 drop in shampoo, 1 more in rinsing water.
Floor cleaners	2% or whatever smells good!
Furniture cleaners	2%

BLENDING CHART

The following gives the amounts of essential oils to add in order to achieve 1, 2 or 3% dilution.

For a 100ml (3½fl oz) bottle:
18–20 drops = 1ml in 100 ml (3½fl oz) bottle = approx 1%
30–40 drops = 2ml in 100 ml (3½fl oz) bottle = approx 2%
54–60 drops = 3ml in 100 ml (3½fl oz) bottle = approx 3%

For a 50ml (1⅔fl oz) bottle:
9–10 drops = 0.5ml in 50ml (1⅔fl oz) bottle = approx 1%
18–20 drops = 1ml in 50ml (1⅔fl oz) bottle = approx 2%
27–30 drops = 1.5ml in 50ml (1⅔fl oz) bottle = approx 3%

For a 10ml (⅓fl oz) bottle:
2 drops in 10ml (⅓fl oz) bottle = approx 1%
4 drops in 10ml (⅓fl oz) bottle = approx 2%
6 drops in 10ml (⅓fl oz) bottle = approx 3%

BODY

AND

SOUL

The inner essence of mankind is magnified and nourished by the use of essential oils. In this chapter everyday living experiences are placed into aromatic perspective. You will come to realise how easy it is to apply aromatherapy to even the most simple events. Once you begin to use the essential oils, they fast become a daily delight and the therapeutic benefits will become obvious.

Credits: Half circular bottle and porcelain dish from The Bay Tree. Herbs from Australian Herb Supplies. Flowers from Lisa Milasas.

THE FACE

All skins are not the same. As babies, we usually have perfect skin: smooth, close textured, moist, plump and with enough oil to protect but not cause a problem. As we get older the conditions under which we live and our age begin to change the texture of our skin and we need to know how to care for our very individual type in order to keep it as close to baby skin as possible.

Here is a list of the main skin types and how to recognise and treat them.

Normal skin

Fairly rare. Normal skin is fine-textured, smooth and soft with no large pores, blackheads, spots, flakes or broken veins apparent. If a tissue is pressed to this skin first thing in the morning there will be only a trace of oil showing. If you are blessed with this type of skin you certainly are among the fortunate few, and should protect it with loving care. Protect it from wind, sun, dry air and air conditioning by using light and gentle moisturisers, cleansers and toners.

Oily skin

If a tissue is pressed to the face first thing in the morning it will show quite a lot of oil. The texture of the skin is coarse with large pores and a tendency to blackheads and spots due to the pores blocking with excessive sebum. The bonus of having oily skin is that it has less tendency to wrinkle than any other type and will get less oily as you get older.

It's a mistake to use harsh soaps and strong astringents containing lots of alcohol in an attempt to control excessive oiliness as these tend to stimulate the skin to produce more sebum and in the long run they make the situation worse.

Oily skin needs an oil-free moisturiser except on the areas around the eyes, throat and lips where a richer moisturiser is needed. This type of skin benefits from regular use of masks and steams to help unblock pores and prevent blackheads forming.

Combination skin

This type is a combination of normal/dry and oily skin. Press a tissue on your face first thing in the morning; if there is a greasy 'T' shape on the tissue this will indicate combination skin. There may be a tendency to blackheads around the nose and pimples on the forehead or chin. There are often small greasy areas on the jawline. The program for this skin has to be oily/normal or oily/dry.

Dry skin

Dry skin is fine textured, delicate and thin with a tendency to line easily. I have skin of this type and rarely use soap and water as it makes my skin feel tight and as if it is going to crack! All masks and steams need to be used with great care as they could encourage broken veins to which this type of skin can be prone.

If you don't want to make 100ml ($3\frac{1}{3}$fl oz) you can use the Blending Chart (page 15) to make 50ml ($1\frac{2}{3}$fl oz) or less.

If you don't have such oils as evening primrose, jojoba or carrot it doesn't matter. It's perfectly all right to use more of the main oil, such as olive or almond, but do try to afford some wheat germ oil (not expensive) and include 5–10% as it acts as a preservative.

OPPOSITE: *Credits: Timber boxes from Linen and Lace of Balmain. Larger scent bottle from Victoria's Old Charm Antiques. Porcelain dish and spoons from The Bay Tree. Fine brush and powder puffs from The Body Shop. Flowers from Lisa Milasas.*

Proportions for Blends

BASE OILS, TO ACT AS A CARRIER

     86% almond oil, olive oil, grape seed oil, safflower oil or other fixed oil.

     5% avocado oil; helps absorption of other oils and is highly nourishing.

     5% wheat germ oil; preservative, nutrient and emollient.

     2% evening primrose oil, jojoba oil, carrot oil; nutrient and emollient.

ADD

     2% essential oils, chosen from those suitable for your skin type.

TOTAL 100%

FACIAL STEAMING

Facial steaming causes the skin to perspire which helps to deep cleanse every pore, it also loosens dead skin scales and grime on the skin. The heat from the steam increases the blood supply and hydrates the skin leaving it looking and feeling softer and more youthful.

Those of you with thread veins on the cheeks need to be careful when steaming. Apply a thick layer of moisture/night cream over the veins and hold your face about 40cm (16in) away from the steam — no closer. Don't steam more than once a fortnight.

If your skin is very dry and sensitive, apply a thin layer of honey over the face and throat before beginning, keep about 40cm (16 inches) between your face and the steam. Don't steam more than once a fortnight.

Normal, combination and oily skins may steam as often as twice a week if liked.

If your tap water is chlorininated, it's wise to use purified water for steaming or, failing this, expose a bowl of tap water to the air for 24 hours to evaporate away the chlorine. The steam from chlorinated water carries chlorine gas which can be harmful.

Steaming Instructions

Have ready a shower cap, a large towel and a heat-proof pad for the table.
1. Wash or cleanse face. Put the shower cap on.
2. Place 1–2 litres (32–64fl oz) of boiling water in a bowl on a heat-proof non-slip mat on the table.
3. Drop 2 drops of essential oil on the surface of the water and quickly form a tent with the towel over the bowl and your head.
4. Keep the face about 20cm (8in) away from the steam and bliss out for about 5–10 minutes. By this time all the deep grime will have floated to the surface.
5. Splash your face with cool (not cold) water and finish with a tonic or astringent and some moisture cream.

Note: Essential oils may be used either singly or in combination with others.

Oils for Normal and Combination Skin

3 drops fennel oil

3 drops lemon oil

6 drops orange oil

6 drops palmarosa oil

3 tablespoons vegetable oil

Mix the oils together well. Pour into a 50ml (1²⁄₃fl oz) bottle. Shake well before use. Use 1 teaspoon of mix for each steam treatment.

Oils for Dry Skin

4 drops chamomile oil

6 drops orange oil

5 drops geranium oil

3 drops palmarosa oil

3 tablespoons vegetable oil

Mix the oils together well. Pour into a 50ml (1²⁄₃fl oz) bottle. Shake well before use. Use 1 teaspoon of mix for each steam treatment.

Oils for Oily Skin

2 drops juniper oil

4 drops lemon grass oil

4 drops lemon oil

4 drops peppermint oil

4 drops sandalwood oil

3 tablespoons vegetable oil

Mix the oils together well. Pour into a 50ml (1²⁄₃fl oz) bottle. Shake well before use. Use 1 teaspoon of mix for each steam treatment.

Oils for Eczema and Problem Skin

6 drops clary sage oil

4 drops fennel oil

6 drops tea tree oil

2 drops thyme oil

3 tablespoons vegetable oil

Mix the oils together well. Pour into a 50ml (1²⁄₃fl oz) bottle. Use as for the above blends.

SCRUBS

Scrubs and masks may be used by people of all ages. They are used for exfoliating, clearing excessive oiliness, refining pores, nourishing dry skin and improving circulation.

The frequency with which you use scrubs and masks depends entirely on your skin type. If you have oily blemished skin you will be able to use these preparations several times a week but if your skin is fine and dry, choose only the most gentle treatment and use it maybe once a fortnight.

Areas with obvious thread veins should never be treated with masks or scrubs as the additional stimulation could worsen the condition.

Almond Scrub

This scrub suits all skin types. This scrub is gentle enough to use often if the almonds are very fine.

2 teaspoons almond oil
1 tablespoon finely ground blanched almonds
1 teaspoon cider vinegar
1 drop basil or lemon oil
purified water

Mix to a paste with the water. Massage gently into the skin, rinse with lukewarm water and pat dry.

Yog 'n' Yeast Scrub

Yeast stimulates the circulation, bringing blood to the surface of the skin. Be very careful when using this scrub not to overstimulate the cheeks where the capillaries are near the surface and quite delicate. If you have a problem with broken veins, avoid the areas or use a more gentle treatment.

Yoghurt cleanses and balances skin pH, almond meal softens and exfoliates, honey deep cleanses, hydrates and has a natural antiseptic action.

1 tablespoon yoghurt
2 teaspoons almond meal
1 teaspoon brewers' yeast
1 teaspoons runny honey
2 drops lavender oil

Mix the ingredients and gently massage into the skin. Rinse off with lukewarm water then pat dry.

MASKS

Masks are very beneficial treatments for all skins. They can improve colour and texture, deep cleanse, remove dead cells from the surface and bring fresh colour and life to sallow skin.

Spread the mask over your face and neck (if you have dry skin or broken veins be very careful as masks may be overstimulating). Lie down on your bed or in the bath and put witch hazel soaked cotton wool soaked in witch hazel or cucumber slices, on your eyes. Now, relax, and let your mind drift for 15–20 minutes. Wash the mask off in lukewarm water followed by a cool splash.

Basic Mask

A basic mask may be made in advance and stored in an airtight jar ready for mixing.

100g (3¹⁄₃oz) fuller's earth or kaolin
2 tablespoons cornflour
1 tablespoon finely ground oats
1 tablespoon finely ground almond meal
20 drops essential oils suitable for your skin type
(see recipes for steaming, page 20)

Mix all the dry ingredients well. Add the essential oils a drop at a time, stirring well to prevent lumping. Mix well and store in a tightly covered jar.

Mix 1 tablespoon of the basic mask to a soft paste with water. Add honey, fruit juice or pulp; vinegar; egg; or oil if liked.

Egg and Lemon Mask

This mask may be used as a cleanser if the wholemeal flour is replaced with arrowroot. It is a deep cleanser which leaves skin feeling soft. If your skin is dry you may replace the lemon juice with orange juice for a gentler action.

1 egg white, beaten
1 teaspoon olive or almond oil
2 teaspoons lemon or orange juice
2 drops lemon or orange oil
wholemeal flour to thicken

Mix well and store in the refrigerator. Use the mask within 3 days.

TONERS

Skin tonics stimulate the circulation and restore the acid mantle to your skin leaving it feeling fresh and clean. Tonics which contain a large amount of alcohol are called astringents; these can dry skin as they remove natural oil. Even very oily skin can suffer from too-frequent applications as the alcohol stimulates the oil glands.

Tonics can be made by adding essential oils to vinegar, alcohol, witch hazel or purified water. Astringents contain the same ingredients but greater quantities of the vinegar, witch hazel or alcohol. A little glycerine may be added to tonics and astringents to counteract any drying effects.

These preparations are suitable for pre-shave and aftershave lotions.

Tonics and Astringents

There are 2 basic methods to apply:

❧ Wet some cotton wool with water and squeeze dry (this prevents waste of your precious lotion). Sprinkle with a few drops of the lotion and stroke the cotton wool upwards over your throat and face.

❧ Press the damp cotton wool flat and fold in half. Pour on a little toner, hold a corner of the wool and slap your face quite briskly (avoiding the cheeks where those delicate veins break really easily).

This treatment brings a nourishing, cleansing blood supply flowing to the skin and gets rid of a sluggish, pasty appearance.

Rose Tonic

This tonic suits all skin types. Rosewater is one of the gentlest, best known skin tonics. You can buy it from any good pharmacy (see page 93).

Witch hazel (see page 94) is another well known tonic, it is stronger than rosewater and should be tested on a small area before using on dry or sensitive skin.

The following is a simple and effective toner for all skins. If your skin is dry you can decrease the witch hazel and increase the rosewater. If you have oily skin you can do the reverse. Shake well before use.

> ¾ cup (185ml/6fl oz) rosewater
> ¼ cup (60ml/2fl oz) witch hazel
> 10 drops palmarosa oil
> 10 drops geranium oil
> ½ teaspoon glycerine

Mix all the ingredients in a bottle then seal.

ASTRINGENTS AND AFTERSHAVES

These are much stronger than tonics and are more suited to oily or combination skins. Alcohol is usually included in astringents. If you can't buy pure ethanol you can use vodka, brandy or other high-proof drinking alcohol.

Citrus Astringent

This delicious astringent will be a hit if given as a gift to someone with oily or combination skin. Men love the spicy perfume and it freshens and smooths skin wonderfully after shaving.

> 20 drops orange oil
> 20 drops lemon oil
> 10 drops peppermint oil
> 5 drops clove oil
> 10 drops cinnamon oil
> 10 drops sandalwood oil
> 2 teaspoons honey
> 1 tablespoon glycerine
> ¾ cup (185ml/6fl oz) 70% proof alcohol
> or vodka
> 1 cup (250ml/8fl oz) purified water

Mix all the ingredients in a jar with a well-fitting lid. Leave in a warm place for a week. Shake often. Strain through coffee filter paper before bottling in amber glass bottles.

Mint Zinger

Another one for the boys. This will leave the face feeling cool and clean. Shake well before use.

> 20 drops peppermint oil
> 20 drops spearmint oil
> 20 drops lemon oil
> 10 drops lavender oil
> 5 drops clove oil
> 1 cup (250ml/8fl oz) purified water
> 1 cup (250ml/8fl oz) witch hazel
> 1 teaspoon glycerine
> 1 teaspoon tincture benzoin

Mix all the ingredients in a jar. Leave for 1 week, shaking often. Strain through coffee filter paper before bottling in amber glass bottles.

NOURISHING OILS

In order to moisturise and soften skin it is necessary to use both oil and water. To receive maximum benefit from the following oils, lightly spray or splash the face with cool water before applying the oil blend suitable for your skin type.

Oil for Dry Skin

1 teaspoon avocado oil

40 drops evening primrose oil

1 teaspoon wheat germ oil

$^1/_3$ cup (80ml/2$^2/_3$fl oz) olive oil

10 drops geranium oil

10 drops lavender oil

5 drops palmarosa oil

5 drops sandalwood oil

5 drops ylang-ylang oil

Place all the ingredients in a 100ml (3$^1/_3$fl oz) bottle. Shake well for several minutes. Leave for 4 days to blend. Store in a cool dark place. Shake before use.

Oil for Oily Skin

Those of you with oily skin will have noticed that there are areas on your face and neck which have little or no oil: these are mainly the throat, lips and under the eyes. Use the oil on these areas but also use a thin smear over the whole face before going to bed as the essential oils have the capacity for balancing and moisturising the skin without encouraging the skin to produce more sebum.

50 drops evening primrose oil

40 drops carrot oil

90ml (3fl oz) grape seed oil

15 drops lemon oil

15 drops geranium oil

5 drops tea tree oil

5 drops juniper oil

Place all the ingredients in a 100ml (3$^1/_3$fl oz) bottle. Shake well for several minutes. Leave for 4 days to blend. Store in a cool dark place. Shake before use.

Oil for Normal Skin

Rarely found after the blessed state of babyhood has been left behind, but those of you fortunate enough to possess firm, smooth, fine-textured skin with no broken veins should make a big effort to keep it this way. This oil will help.

2 teaspoons avocado oil

40 drops jojoba oil

1 teaspoon wheat germ oil

$^1/_3$ cup (80ml/2$^2/_3$fl oz) almond oil

15 drops lavender oil

10 drops geranium oil

10 drops chamomile oil

5 drops sandalwood oil

Place all the ingredients in a 100ml (3$^1/_3$fl oz) bottle. Shake well for several minutes. Leave for 4 days to blend. Store in a cool dark place. Shake well before use.

Oil for Sensitive Skin

This oil blend contains only the gentlest oils. Nevertheless, test all the oils on your skin before blending and using on your face.

1 teaspoon avocado oil

60 drops evening primrose oil

40 drops wheat germ oil

$^1/_3$ cup (80ml/2$^2/_3$fl oz) apricot kernel oil

10 drops geranium oil

5 drops chamomile oil

5 drops palmarosa oil

Place all the ingredients in a 100ml (3$^1/_3$fl oz) bottle. Shake well for several minutes. Leave for 4 days to blend. Store in a cool dark place. Shake before use.

AROUND THE EYES

The skin around the eyes shows early lines in the same way as the neck. Crow's-feet, bags under the eyes and dark circles can be very demoralising — laughter lines are a different matter.

Remember that the skin around the eyes is fragile and harm can be done if you are heavy-handed. Use the middle finger to gently pat oils and lotions on this area. Avoid using heavy oils.

Under-Eye Oil

This is a very fine oil which will soften and smooth the wrinkles and skin. Use the tiniest amount possible and pat on gently with the middle finger.

2 x 250mg capsules vitamin E oil
40ml (1 $^1/_3$fl oz) almond oil
15 drops evening primrose oil
5 drops carrot oil
5 drops borage seed oil
10 drops lavender oil

Puncture the vitamin E capsules and squeeze into the combined other oils. Mix together and pour into a 50ml (1 $^2/_3$fl oz) bottle. Shake well.

A drop under each eye is enough. Apply the oil at night, leave for 10 minutes and carefully blot the excess with a tissue. Avoid getting this oil into the eye itself or it will sting and could be harmful.

LIPS AND TEETH

Lips should always be kissable but unfortunately are often plagued with cold sores, cracks, lines and dryness. Use this cream at night and during the day if you don't use lipstick.

Coconut and Lemon Lip Salve

24g ($^2/_3$oz or 2 cubes) beeswax
2 tablespoons wheat germ oil
$^1/_3$ cup (80ml/2 $^2/_3$fl oz) coconut oil
20 drops almond oil
4 x 250mg capsules vitamin E oil
30 drops lemon oil
$^1/_2$ teaspoon glycerine (optional)

Melt the beeswax gently in a double boiler. Add the wheat germ, coconut and almond oils. Don't overheat. Pierce the vitamin E capsules and squeeze in. Add the lemon oil. Stir well.

Mix the glycerine in until completely incorporated. Pot quickly while still soft.

MOUTHWASHES

Depending on the formulation, mouthwashes can be used to sweeten the breath, keep bacteria and fungus infections at bay and ensure healthy gums.

Quickie Mouthwash

A teaspoon of cider vinegar and 1 drop of peppermint or clove oil in a glass of water will freshen the mouth.

Myrrh Mouthwash

Myrrh helps to heal mouth ulcers.

$^1/_3$ cup (80ml/2 $^2/_3$fl oz) sherry
2 tablespoons cider vinegar
1 teaspoon honey
10 drops peppermint oil
3 drops clove oil
5 drops tincture of myrrh

Mix all the ingredients in a jar and steep for a week, shaking often. Strain well through coffee filter paper then bottle. Add 1 teaspoon of the mouthwash to $^1/_4$ glass of water and rinse mouth well several times with the mixture; spit out.

Lemon and Mint Mouthwash

This mouthwash will keep the mouth healthy and sweet smelling. It will also help to cure sore or ulcerated mouths. Don't swallow the mixture.

50ml (1 $^2/_3$fl oz) sherry
3 tablespoons vodka or brandy
1 drop thyme oil
5 drops lemon oil
5 drops peppermint oil
2 drops lavender oil
2 drops tea tree oil
1 teaspoon glycerine

Mix all ingredients in a jar; stand 1 week. Strain through coffee filter paper. Add 1 teaspoon of the mouthwash to $^1/_2$ glass of warm water and rinse mouth several times with the mixture; spit out.

ACNE

This distressing and disfiguring complaint is mainly a teenage problem but can occur in older people as well.

Teenage acne usually starts at puberty. There are many hormonal changes happening within the body at this time. As with most skin problems, acne treatment begins within the body.

Following are some choices you can make for yourself for a healthy body and healthy skin.

- Make sure your bowels are regular.
- Eat lots of raw and cooked vegetables daily.
- Cut out/down junk food.
- Take a multi-vitamin capsule plus extra vitamin B6, vitamin E and C and 15mg zinc and evening primrose capsules daily.
- Have some exercise every day as this increases circulation which brings healing nutrients and oxygen to the skin in increased quantities.
- Drink 6–8 glasses of purified water a day.
- Treat your face to 10 minutes of sunlight every day, preferably in the early morning or late afternoon.
- Drastically reduce salt intake.
- Talk to a doctor about Retin A therapy.
- Before breakfast, drink a glass of water containing the juice of 1 lemon with no sweetener.
- Learn to relax. Join a stress management or meditation group; spend time peacefully alone; budget time for fun.
- Wash the face 3 times a day using very mild soap which contains glycerine, then rinse well with lukewarm water then pat dry using a fresh towel each time if any weeping spots.
- Try to avoid using make-up or cover make-up. I know that this is hard but you stand a better chance of healing if you do this. Use only the Herbal Healing Day Oil (see this page) and Herbal Healing Night Oil on your skin.
- Have a facial steam once or twice a week using the Cleansing Facial Steam (see opposite).
- Never but never be tempted to squeeze a pimple. The result of this type of interference will be scarring and a spread of infection.

Palmarosa Rinse Lotion

90ml (3fl oz) cider vinegar
15 drops palmarosa oil
15 drops tea tree oil
2 teaspoons tincture of myrrh

Place all ingredients in a 100ml (3⅓fl oz) bottle.
Shake well for several minutes. Leave for 4 days to blend. Store in a cool dark place.
Shake mixture before using. Add 1 teaspoon to 1 cup warm water and use as a face rinse.

Herbal Healing Day Oil

This gentle but powerful oil is for day treatment of acne, pimples or otherwise infected skin.

40ml (1⅓fl oz) almond oil
20 drops carrot oil
5 drops tea tree oil
10 drops palmarosa oil
2 drops thyme oil
5 drops geranium oil

Place all ingredients in a 50ml (1⅔fl oz) bottle, shake well for several minutes. Leave for 4 days to blend. Store in a cool dark place.
Shake mixture before using. Place 3–4 drops on the palm of your hand, dip the fingers in and gently smooth over skin. Don't get any in your eyes as it stings. Leave on for 5–10 minutes, blot surplus off with tissue. Use morning and midday.

Herbal Healing Night Oil

This blend feels a little oilier than its daytime companion but don't worry; these oils heal and regenerate while you sleep.

40ml (1⅓fl oz) almond oil
20 drops carrot oil
20 drops evening primrose oil
5 drops tea tree oil
5 drops palmarosa or lavender oil

Place all ingredients in a 50ml (1⅔fl oz) bottle, shake well for several minutes. Leave for 4 days to blend. Store in a cool dark place. Shake before use. Apply as for Herbal Healing Day oil.

Cleansing Facial Steam

The antibacterial action of this treatment combined with the heat from the steam will draw impurities to the surface, so don't use it before a big date!

1 teaspoon palmarosa oil

1 teaspoon lavender oil

1/2 teaspoon tea tree oil

20 drops thyme oil

30 drops geranium oil

Place all the ingredients in a 15ml (1/2fl oz) bottle. Shake well and leave for 4 days to blend.

Shake, then add 5–10 drops of the blend to a bowl of boiling water. Cover your head with a towel forming a tent. Keep your face about 35cm (14in) from the steam and stay for 5 minutes.

BLACKHEADS

When the sebaceous glands oversecrete and the excess sebum doesn't move out of the duct a blackhead results. This can become a problem if not carefully dealt with, as the pore can become infected if the blackhead is roughly removed and the area isn't disinfected. Facial scrubs are useful in the prevention of the formation of blackheads.

The safest way to remove blackheads is to steam the skin, using boiling water and an antiseptic oil to prevent infection. This loosens the sebum and relaxes the pores.

1. Three-quarters fill a bowl with boiling water.

2. Place 1 drop tea tree oil and 2 drops geranium oil on the water and cover your head with a towel forming a tent around the bowl and your head.

3. Steam for about 10 minutes keeping your face about 30cm (12in) away from the water.

4. Pat your skin dry and with cotton wool wrapped round your nails, gently press the skin on either side of the blackhead until it pops out, or use a little tool for extracting blackheads, available from cosmetic counters or pharmacies.

5. Splash the skin with the following mixture which will help to shrink and disinfect the pore.

Astringent Lotion

2 tablespoons purified water

2 teaspoons witch hazel

1 drop palmarosa oil

2 drops cypress oil

Place all the ingredients in a 50ml (1 2/3fl oz) jar. Shake well before using.

BELOW: *Credits: Wire basket from The Bay Tree. Flowers from Lisa Milasas.*

HANDS

Essential oils are particularly good for hands as they work very quickly and are readily absorbed without leaving a greasy feeling. These hard-working parts of our bodies need all the love and care we can give them.

The following oil is a luxurious treat for the tools we use most often and usually appreciate the least.

Lemon and Lavender Hand Softener

If your hands are really rough, use this rich cream during the evening while talking or watching television, or massage a goodly amount on before bedtime and cover the hands with cotton gloves to protect the bedclothes. This is a cream for dry, rough, work-worn hands. Massage it into the hands before doing dirty jobs.

3 cubes (45g/1 ½oz) beeswax
⅓ cup (80ml/2⅔fl oz) almond oil
½ cup (125ml/4fl oz) olive oil
2 tablespoons glycerine
2 droppers lemon oil
2 droppers lavender oil

Melt the first 4 ingredients gently in a double boiler. Stir in the glycerine until completely blended. Drip the essential oils into the slightly cooled mixture. Stir mixture very well then pot.

FEET

Feet are the unsung heroes who carry us, more or less uncomplainingly, on our journey through possibly eighty years. We usually give them attention only if they ache or grow corns.

We abuse our feet with ill-fitting shoes, synthetic shoes, stockings or socks; by cutting toe nails incorrectly, weighing too much and standing for too long. Let's give a thought and a cheer to the feet and promise them a bit of loving care.

Vinegar Foot Soother

If your work involves a lot of standing, your feet are probably aching and swollen when you get home. Make the following herbal vinegar and use very cold for the most soothing effect.

2 cups (500ml/16fl oz) white vinegar
20 drops bay oil
20 drops lavender oil
20 drops black pepper oil
10 drops thyme oil
20 drops rosemary oil

Mix all the ingredients together in a large bottle. Shake well for several minutes. Store for 4 days before using. Dab on the feet and air dry.

Foot Restore Foot Bath

This is another soothing treatment for aching feet. Try to relax as much as possible while enjoying this experience; listen to music or read a book.

Half fill 2 bowls, each large enough for both feet — one with water as hot as you can bear and the other with cold water. Soak feet in the hot water for 10–15 minutes.

Sprinkle 1 drop lavender oil, 1 drop cypress oil and 1 drop rosemary oil on the surface of the cold water. Agitate to disperse. Soak the feet for a few minutes then pat dry.

Herb Oil Foot Powder

Sprinkle this powder inside socks and shoes if you suffer from sweaty or smelly feet. This helps to cure athlete's foot and absorb perspiration.

50g (1⅔oz) kaolin
25g (⅔oz) cornflour
25g (⅔oz) talcum powder
10 drops sage oil
10 drops rosemary oil
20 drops lavender oil
10 drops myrrh oil

Mix the dry indredients in a bowl then add the combined oils a drop at a time. The powder will lump if the oils are added too quickly.

OPPOSITE: *Credits: Wire soap holder from Linen and Lace of Balmain. Bath brush and loofa from The Body Shop. Flowers from Lisa Milasas.*

BETTER HAIR

Very few people are satisfied with their hair in spite of the fact that both women and men spend an increasing amount of time and money in hairdressing salons and pharmacies pursuing a dream of thick, glossy hair. The time and money would be far better spent in your own kitchens making real, honest-to-goodness, preparations which will really improve the condition and appearance of the hair.

HAIR TREATMENTS

The pH of hair is slightly acidic in the same way as skin but there is no such thing as an acidic shampoo as alkalinity is needed to de-grease hair. Soaps and shampoos are alkaline by nature which enables them to do a good cleaning job but the alkalinity also causes the overlapping scales on the hair shaft to open and separate. The hair then has a tendency to lawlessness, standing away from the scalp and having a lacklustre, fly-away appearance.

It's important that rinses and conditioners are mildly acidic to counteract the alkalinity of the shampoo and to cause the overlapping scales on the hair shaft to close and lie flat and overlapping once more. When this happens the hair has a shiny, smooth appearance and the inside of the hair shaft is protected.

The following recipes are for natural pre-shampoo treatments, shampoos, rinses and conditioners which may take a little getting used to but which will reward you with the best head of hair to ever crown you.

PRE-SHAMPOO TREATMENTS

Oil and Honey

For dry, damaged and fine hair

1 beaten egg yolk
1 tablespoon olive oil
1 teaspoon runny honey
4 drops lavender or basil oil
dried milk powder

Mix ingredients to a soft paste with the dried milk. Massage gently into hair, cover hair with plastic shower cap or hot, wet towel. Leave 20 minutes. Shampoo with mild herbal shampoo.

Egg and Lemon

For oily hair

1 beaten egg
1 teaspoon runny honey
1 tablespoon lemon juice
1 tablespoon water
2 drops lemon oil
2 drops geranium oil
dried milk powder to mix

Mix ingredients well to a soft paste. Massage gently into hair, cover hair with plastic shower cap or hot, wet towel. Leave 20 minutes. Shampoo with mild herbal shampoo.

SHAMPOOS

Herb Oil Shampoo

By making up a quantity of the following base mixture each member of the family will be able to devise their own tailor made shampoo by adding essential oils suited to their hair type.

Basic Shampoo Base

80–100g (2⅔–3⅓oz) soap flakes (e.g. Lux)
1 litre (32fl oz) rain or purified water, heated
2 teaspoons borax

Mix all the ingredients until dissolved. Cool and pour into a large jar. Mix well before using.

Mix one of the essential oil blends on page 32 (100 drops) with 1 cup (250ml/8fl oz) of this basic mixture and blend really well. A beaten egg, lanolin or gelatin may be mixed into the shampoo just prior to use.

The basic mixture may go lumpy on standing but, just give a good stir until blended. This amount will provide enough for several shampoos.

OIL BLENDS TO USE WITH BASIC SHAMPOO BASE

These blends may be made in larger quantities and used in the rinse as well as the shampoo.

Dry Hair

40 drops lavender oil
25 drops geranium oil
25 drops rosemary oil
10 drops sandalwood oil

Normal Hair

30 drops rosemary oil
30 drops lavender oil
20 drops basil oil
20 drops lemon oil

Oily Hair

40 drops lemon oil
30 drops rosemary oil
20 drops lavender oil
10 drops cypress oil

Dandruff

30 drops lemon oil
30 drops tea tree oil
20 drops lavender oil
10 drops thyme oil
10 drops basil oil

Damaged, or Dry Fine Hair

50 drops chamomile oil
30 drops lavender oil
10 drops carrot oil
10 drops clary sage oil

CONDITIONERS

The following conditioners don't put layers of silicon on the hair shaft and they will leave your hair full-bodied, soft and glossy.

Rosemary Conditioner

For all hair types except oily

1 beaten egg
1 teaspoon glycerine
2 drops castor oil
2 drops rosemary oil
2 drops lavender oil
skim milk powder

Beat all ingredients together adding enough milk powder to form a soft paste. Massage into the hair after shampooing, leave on the hair for a few minutes then rinse lightly with lukewarm water.

Brandy Lemon Conditioner

For oily hair

2 tablespoons brandy
1 teaspoon runny honey
1 beaten egg
2 drops lemon grass oil
1 drop rosemary oil
skim milk powder

Beat all the ingredients together with enough milk powder to form a soft paste. Massage into the hair after shampooing, leave on the hair for a few minutes then rinse lightly with lukewarm water.

BATHS

TYPES OF BATHS

HOT BATHS: 38–40°C (100–104°F) for 10–15 minutes only. This bath increases perspiration and the rate of breathing, reduces fevers and eliminates toxins. Wrap up in blankets after the bath and drink the appropriate herb teas during and after.

WARM BATHS: 27–34°C (80–93°F). Soak for 20–60 minutes. This bath is calming and relaxing.

COLD BATHS: 21–27°C (70–80°F) soak for 2–5 minutes only. This bath improves breathing and muscle tone, decreases fatigue, improves thyroid function, tones skin and relieves constipation.

BATHING WITH HERB OILS

Don't be tempted to use more than 8–10 drops of essential oil in a full bath.

To avoid floating unmixed oil it's best to mix the oils with either 1 tablespoon full cream milk or almond oil before adding.

Run the bath and add the oils just before getting into the bath or the precious essences may evaporate before you can get the full benefit.

Oil Suggestions For Baths

ANTIBACTERIAL: 3 drops tea tree oil, 3 drops eucalyptus oil, 2 drops thyme oil, 1 drop lemon oil, 1 drop clove oil

ANTIVIRAL: 3 drops tea tree oil, 3 drops eucalyptus oil, 3 drops lavender oil, 1 drop thyme oil

DEODORISING: 4 drops sage oil, 2 drops eucalyptus oil, 2 drops tea tree oil, 2 drops peppermint oil

DRY SKIN: 4 drops chamomile oil, 4 drops geranium oil, 2 drops patchouli oil

GREASY SKIN: 5 drops lemon oil, 3 drops ylang-ylang oil, 2 drops cypress oil

SPOTTY SKIN: 2 drops eucalyptus oil, 2 drops thyme oil, 4 drops lavender oil, 2 drops chamomile oil

HEAD CLEARING: 2 drops peppermint oil, 2 drops lemon oil, 1 drop thyme oil, 2 drops rosemary oil, 3 drops lavender oil

HYDRATING: 2 drops chamomile oil, 2 drops lavender oil, 2 drops carrot oil, 2 drops geranium oil, 2 drops rose oil (optional)

JUST-AHHHHH!: 1 drop lavender oil, 2 drops grapefruit oil, 2 drops geranium oil, 2 drops ylang-ylang oil, 2 drops patchouli oil

REJUVENATING: 4 drops lavender oil, 3 drops rosemary oil, 2 drops peppermint oil

RELAXING: 4 drops chamomile oil, 3 drops lavender oil, 3 drops ylang-ylang oil

RISE AND SHINE: 2 drops bergamot oil, 3 drops orange oil, 3 drops lemon oil, 1 drop peppermint oil, 1 drop cinnamon oil

SLIMMING: 3 drops sage oil, 3 drops petitgrain oil, 2 drops grapefruit oil, 2 drops lavender oil

MILD SUN BURN: 8–10 drops lavender oil

Bath Lotions and Vinegars

Nothing is cheaper, easier or more satisfying to make than these herbal vinegars. Vinegar restores the acid mantle to skin, relieves dryness, itching and the pain of sunburn. Cider vinegar seems to have the most therapeutic properties but a good quality white vinegar can be used. For skin tonics white wine vinegar is more gentle and refined.

If you really hate the smell of vinegar you can substitute vodka (mixed equally with water) or white wine. These last two are more expensive but the perfume of the oils is more apparent.

The bath herbal vinegars listed below may also be used as:

HAIR RINSES: Add ½ cup (125ml/4fl oz) of bath vinegar to 4 cups 1 litre (32fl oz) water

SKIN TONICS: Add 1 tablespoon of bath vinegar to ½ cup (125ml/4fl oz) water

AFTER-SHOWER FRICTION RUB: Add ½ cup (125ml/4fl oz) of bath vinegar to 1 cup (250ml/8fl oz) of water

DEODORANT: Use undiluted

Herbal Bath Vinegar

Mix 500ml (16fl oz) cider or white wine vinegar with 100 drops mixed or single essential oil Choose from the following blends.

Lavender

100 drops lavender oil

Citrus Sensation

30 drops lemon oil
25 drops petitgrain oil
20 drops bergamot oil
20 drops orange oil
5 drops clove oil

Mint Tang

40 drops peppermint oil
40 drops spearmint oil
15 drops lavender oil
5 drops clove oil

Herb Spice

40 drops clary sage oil
40 drops rosemary oil
10 drops fennel oil
10 drops anise oil

Forest Fantasy

40 drops pine oil
20 drops hyssop oil
20 drops lemon oil
10 drops cypress oil
10 drops peppermint oil

OPPOSITE: Credits: Towelling face cloths and bath brush from The Body Shop. Wire basket from The Bay Tree. Huckerback face cloth from Linen and Lace of Balmain. Flowers from Lisa Milasas.

BUBBLE BATHS

Bubble baths are fun and have a luxurious feeling but one should not indulge for too long or too often as the base of most commercial bubble baths is the cheapest available detergent and can overdry the skin. Use only the amount recommended and use a massage oil after the bath to counteract the drying effects. The addition of honey, glycerine or oil to recipes counteracts the drying effect of the detergent. You can make your own superior product by using a good shampoo or the best quality detergent available.

Perfume Oil Bubble Bath

The oils for this recipe can be chosen from the suggestions for Herbal Bath Vinegar (see left).

¼ cup (60ml/2fl oz) olive or almond oil
1 cup (250ml/8fl oz) good quality shampoo or detergent
4 droppers essential oil

Mix all ingredients together very thoroughly. Bottle and invert bottle several times to mix contents before using. Slowly trickle ¼–½ cup (60ml/2fl oz–125ml/4fl oz) of the mixture under a fast running tap to maximise the bubbles.

BATH CREAM

This cream needs refrigeration and should be used within 2 weeks. It is easy to make and leaves the skin soft and moisturised. Don't add it to very hot water or the egg will set and go stringy. The oil disperses in the water and doesn't leave a greasy ring around the bath.

Lavender Cream

1 egg
½ cup (125ml/4fl oz) olive oil
1 tablespoon glycerine
½ cup (50g/1²⁄₃oz) dried milk powder
10 drops of carrot oil
10 drops orange oil
20 drops lavender oil
2 cups (500ml/16fl oz) water

Beat the egg, olive oil, glycerine and dried milk together in a bowl. Add the oils while beating. Beat the water in, a little at a time. Store in the refrigerator. Add ¼–½ cup (60ml/2fl oz– 125ml/4fl oz) to bath water. Swoosh to disperse.

BATH SALTS

Bath salts are used primarily to soften hard water and may also contain essential oils to perfume the water and add therapeutic properties. If you would like to colour the salts you can add a few drops of natural colouring drop by drop after adding the oils.

Old Fashioned Girl

100g (3¹⁄₃oz) tartaric acid
100g (3¹⁄₃oz) bicarbonate of soda
50g (1²⁄₃oz) arrowroot powder
4 drops lavender oil
2 drops clove oil
4 drops sandalwood oil

Mix the powders together well. Add the oils drop by drop, stirring all the time to prevent caking.

Place all in a jar and shake daily for a few days. Sprinkle ¼–½ cup (60ml/2fl oz–125ml/4fl oz) into the bath as it is running.

BATH OIL

Sleep Well Bath Oil

This oil is semi-dispersible which means the oil will almost dissolve in the bath water.

1 cup (250ml/
8fl oz) brandy or vodka
2 teaspoons chamomile oil
1 teaspoon lavender oil
1 teaspoon marjoram oil
1 teaspoon sandalwood oil
3 teaspoons glycerine

Mix all the ingredients together in a bottle and shake well. Add ½–1 teaspoon to the bath; anymore and you might overdose on the powerful fragrance or you may even become enlightened and float off the planet! You'll find your sleep will be refreshing.

DEODORANTS

Fresh perspiration has little odour but as it decomposes it develops mild to yuck smells. The strength of perspiration odour seems to be determined by many factors: puberty or other hormonal changes; high intake of meat, junk foods or alcohol; stress. Synthetic clothing doesn't allow the body to breath or perspiration to evaporate and this compounds the problem.

The following deodorants aren't as strong as the commercial varieties but are very nice to use and don't contain any dubious ingredients.

Deodorant Powder

This deodorant powder may be patted on the underarms, under the breasts, in the groin area, on the feet or anywhere that perspiration is a problem.

3 tablespoons orris root powder
6 tablespoons talcum powder
3 tablespoons arrowroot powder
$^1/_2$ teaspoon ground cloves
1 tablespoon ground coriander seed

30 drops lavender oil
20 drops rosemary oil
10 drops patchouli oil
10 drops lemon oil
5 drops clove oil

Mix the powders together in a large bowl. Sieve. Mix the oils together. Add, a drop at a time to the powders stirring constantly or the powder will go lumpy. Store in airtight containers.

Deodorant Lotion

50ml (1$^2/_3$fl oz) vodka
20ml ($^2/_3$fl oz) witch hazel
10ml ($^1/_3$fl oz) almond oil
1 teaspoon glycerine
30 drops sage oil
20 drops lavender oil
20 drops peppermint oil
10 drops patchouli oil
10 drops sandalwood oil

Blend all the ingredients in a 100ml (3$^1/_3$fl oz) bottle. Shake well to mix and leave for 4 days before using. Shake before use.

MASSAGE OILS

Anyone who has experienced an aromatherapy massage will know what an uplifting experience it is. It's obviously more relaxing to receive a massage from a friend or a masseur but, failing this, you can obtain all the benefits from the oils by massaging them over the entire body after a bath or shower. A teaspoon or so will probably be enough for your whole body and this amount won't leave you feeling greasy.

BASIC MASSAGE OIL

To make 100ml (3⅓fl oz) massage oil, the following formula may be followed but the types of oils can be changed depending on availability and individual need.

70ml (2⅓fl oz) grape seed oil
2 teaspoons almond oil
2 teaspoons avocado oil
1 teaspoon wheat germ oil
essential oils (see blends this page)

Mix all the ingredients together in a 100ml (3⅓fl oz) bottle. Shake well to mix.

The following recipes are suggestions of suitable blends of essential oils to use in the Basic Massage Oil. The bath blends listed in the Baths section may also be used for massage oils.

Aching Bodies

A good blend to use for an after-sport massage

2 teaspoons lavender oil
1 teaspoon rosemary oil
1 teaspoon sage oil
½ teaspoon peppermint oil
½ teaspoon cypress oil

Mix all the oils in a 25ml (about 1fl oz) bottle then add 40 drops to a 100ml (3⅓fl oz) bottle of Basic Massage Oil. Shake well to mix. Leave for 4 days to blend.

Aching Minds

When you are tired from thinking and worrying, this blend will iron your mind smooth

1 teaspoon lavender oil
2 teaspoons geranium oil
1 teaspoon rose geranium oil
½ teaspoon cedarwood oil
½ teaspoon peppermint oil

Mix all the oils in a 25ml (about 1fl oz) bottle then add 40 drops to a 100ml (3⅓fl oz) bottle of Basic Massage Oil. Shake well to mix. Leave for 4 days to blend.

Sleep Well

To relieve stress and ensure a good night's sleep, use this blend either in a bath or for a gentle massage given by a gentle friend

2 teaspoons chamomile oil
1 teaspoon lavender oil
1 teaspoon marjoram oil
1 teaspoon sandalwood oil

Mix all the oils in a 25ml (about 1fl oz) bottle then add 40 drops to a 100ml (3⅓fl oz) bottle of Basic Massage Oil. Shake well to mix. Leave for 4 days to blend.

Rheumatoid Arthritis

Massage is a useful part of an all-over treatment for this painful complaint

2 teaspoons chamomile oil

1 teaspoon lavender oil

½ teaspoon sage oil

½ teaspoon lemon oil

½ teaspoon geranium oil

½ teaspoon thyme oil

Mix all the oils in a 25ml (about 1fl oz) bottle then add 40 drops to a 100ml (3⅓fl oz) bottle of Basic Massage Oil. Shake well to mix. Leave for 4 days to blend.

Osteoarthritis

2 teaspoons marjoram oil

1 teaspoon lemon oil

1 teaspoon thyme oil

1 teaspoon eucalyptus oil

Mix all the oils in a 25ml (about 1fl oz) bottle then add 40 drops to a 100ml (3⅓fl oz) bottle of Basic Massage Oil. Shake well to mix. Leave for 4 days to blend.

Credits: Massage rollers from The Body Shop. Porcelain dish from The Bay Tree. Flowers from Lisa Milasas.

MOTHER AND CHILD

There should be no more satisfying and special time in a woman's life than the nine months of pregnancy but women are often beset by anxiety and discomfort. This is a time to take the ultimate care of yourself to help to ensure that you and your baby are as healthy as it is possible to be.

The use of essential oils during pregnancy, labour and after delivery can help immeasurably, both physically and emotionally.

The recipes in this section are for external use only as specific advice should be obtained before taking internal remedies when pregnant. There are many herbs which are valuable and which a competent herbalist will prescribe for you.

It's a good idea to begin to massage the nipples for a couple of months before the birth. Massaging will help to avoid the painfully cracked nipples from which so many mothers suffer and which change the joyful time of breast feeding into a miserable experience.

The essential oils will pass through the skin and be experienced by your baby so don't be tempted to either increase or change the recommended oils. There are some oils which should never be used during pregnancy.

OILS WHICH MAY BE UNSAFE TO USE DURING PREGNANCY INCLUDE: Basil, cedarwood, clary sage, fennel, hyssop, juniper, marjoram, pennyroyal, peppermint, rosemary, thyme.

RECOMMENDED OILS FOR USE DURING PREGNANCY INCLUDE: Benzoin, chamomile, cypress, geranium, ginger, grapefruit, jasmine, lavender, lemon, mandarin, palmarosa, patchouli, rose, ylang-ylang.

RECOMMENDED OILS FOR USE DURING LABOUR INCLUDE: Clary sage, geranium, jasmine, lavender, neroli.

RECOMMENDED OILS FOR POST-NATAL CARE INCLUDE: Chamomile, clary sage, fennel, frankincense, geranium, grapefruit, lavender, patchouli.

THE PREGNANCY
Morning Sickness

The following suggestions should work very quickly to dispel morning sickness. The scent of the spearmint will calm your tummy during the night and you should wake up with no nasty queasiness. Use any or all of the following ideas.

 Put a drop of spearmint oil on the light globe before switching on the bedroom light at night.

 Put another two drops on cotton wool and tuck it under your pillow.

 Place a small bowl of lukewarm water in the bedroom before going to bed. Sprinkle with 1 drop of spearmint and 2 drops of lavender oil.

Stretch Marks

As soon as pregnancy is confirmed it's time to start taking extra care of the skin on the tummy, thighs, bottom and breasts. Stretch marks can be largely avoided but not easily cured and the use of these oils morning and night will certainly help to keep the constantly and rapidly stretching skin supple and pliable.

2 x 250mg vitamin E capsules
150ml (5fl oz) almond oil
15ml ($\frac{1}{2}$fl oz) olive oil
15ml ($\frac{1}{2}$fl oz) carrot oil
10ml ($\frac{1}{3}$fl oz) avocado oil
1 teaspoon wheat germ oil
10 drops mandarin oil
10 drops palmarosa oil
20 drops lavender oil

Pierce the vitamin E capsules and squeeze the oil into a 200ml (6$\frac{2}{3}$fl oz) bottle. Add the remaining oils and shake well to mix. Shake the bottle well before use. Massage the oil thoroughly into the skin of the breasts and from the waist down to the knees.

Nipples

This nipple oil is suitable to use from the time you know that you are pregnant and until after the baby is born.

40ml (1$\frac{1}{3}$fl oz) almond oil
1 teaspoon wheat germ oil
$\frac{1}{2}$ teaspoon carrot oil
15 drops chamomile oil

Mix all the oils in a 50ml (1$\frac{2}{3}$fl oz) bottle. Shake well. Leave for 4 days to blend. Massage well into the nipples and surrounding areas using thumb and forefingers in a firm but gentle squeezing motion. Wash all traces of oil away thoroughly before breast-feeding your baby.

Aching Backs

Towards the end of pregnancy can be a trying time as the body gets heavier and backaches more frequent. This oil is very gentle and will help to alleviate the depressing dragging feeling. If used regularly it may help to prevent the backache.

50ml (1$\frac{2}{3}$fl oz) grapeseed oil
45ml (1 1$\frac{2}{3}$fl oz) almond oil
10 drops chamomile oil
15 drops lavender oil

Mix all the oils together in a 100ml (3$\frac{1}{3}$fl oz) bottle. Shake well. Leave for 4 days to blend. Ask a friend or partner to massage your lower back very gently with the blend after you have bathed.

Varicose Veins

Varicose veins are largely hereditary so if members of your family suffer from them, take precautionary measures as early as possible.

- Try to avoid standing for long periods.
- Go for 2 walks a day. Even short walks help.
- If possible, raise the foot of the bed (not if it gives you indigestion though).
- At least once a day lie down for 10 minutes with your feet higher than your head. You will find it more comfortable if you have a little pillow under your head and one under the lower back.
- Use support pantihose in preference to ordinary ones.
- Stroke the following oil on your legs twice a day starting at the ankle, stroking firmly but gently upwards. In the later stages of pregnancy it will be difficult and you may need a partner or friend to do this for you.

30ml (1fl oz) grape seed oil
15ml ($\frac{1}{2}$fl oz) almond oil
15 drops geranium oil
5 drops lemon oil
5 drops cypress oil

Mix all the oils together in a 50ml (1$\frac{2}{3}$fl oz) bottle. Leave for 4 days to blend.

Nerves and Depression

It's very natural for you to feel conflicting emotions during pregnancy. Your body is undergoing immense changes and this, combined with tiredness, can result in tearfulness and the miseries. When this happens, stop what you are doing and have a bath! During my 5 pregnancies I often relied on a bath to see me through the day. The water supports your tummy and removes the heavy feeling while the warm water (not hot) with essential oils takes away the gloominess.

Choose a time when the other children are at school or ask a friend or relative to mind young children for an hour or so.

If you don't own a bath pillow, fill a hot water bottle with warm water and tuck it under your neck, the warmth will help you to really relax.

Use a maximum of 6 drops of essential oil and choose from: lavender, geranium, cypress, ylang-ylang. Add the oils after running the bath and swoosh the water to disperse the drops.

The Birth

This is it! Soon you will see the baby who has been your constant companion for 9 months.

There are a few oils which are going to help you to welcome your baby into the world. You are going to be working very hard for the time the journey will take from the womb to the world and the following massage blend will: help to lessen the discomfort of contractions, gently speed up contractions, create a calm atmosphere, help to keep you and the surrounding air free of bacteria.

10ml (1/3fl oz) grape seed oil
10ml (1/3fl oz) almond oil
5 drops clary sage oil
5 drops lavender oil
5 drops geranium oil
3 drops neroli or rose oil (please try to afford one of these oils for this very special occasion!)

Mix all the oils together in a 25ml (about 1fl oz) bottle. Shake well and leave for 4 days to blend.

Massage the oil blend on the back as often as liked during the labour. If it can be tolerated, the abdomen can be massaged once during the first stage using only the lightest strokes.

After the Birth

Now you have your baby and will be having a wonderful time getting to know each other. This time can be stressful and demanding though and the essential oils can help you to avoid or banish some of the annoying problems which occasionally arise.

The choice of oils is still limited as breast fed babies will receive these oils in the breast milk.

To Increase Milk Flow

24ml (5/6fl oz) grape seed oil
6 drops fennel oil
6 drops clary sage oil

Mix all the oils together in a 25ml (about 1fl oz) bottle. Shake well. Leave for 4 days to blend.

Massage the oil blend gently into the breasts using a circular movement. Wash off thoroughly before breast-feeding.

Post-Natal Blues Beater

Mix any combination of the following oils to create a perfume which is pleasing to you. It will dispel depression, revitalise and relax: bergamot, geranium, grapefruit, lemon, frankincense, lavender, jasmine.

Use 8 drops of the blend in the bath; in room sprays (see page 15); in a massage oil base (see page 38) or any of the suggestions in this book.

Newborn Babies

Babies deserve the best. By using pure, natural oils on their bodies we are giving them just that. The best base oils for baby are virgin olive oil and almond oil; these can be mixed and used alone for the first 2 days. Commercial baby oil is mainly mineral oil and really not good for anyone and certainly not on new and tender skin.

Most essential oils are too powerful to use on newborn babies and there are very few which are safe to use until the baby is at least between 2 and 3 months old.

Chamomile and lavender oil may be used for babies after the first 48 hours. These 2 oils calm the nervous system, boost the immune system and are antibacterial and mildly antiviral. These oils may also be used in the bedroom to soothe babies who are restless, 'scratchy' or suffering from colds. A drop of either of the oils in a diffuser or floating in a bowl of warm water near the cot should help to ensure restful sleep.

NOTE: Never exceed the amount of essential oil suggested in a recipe.

Babies love to be massaged. Massaging creates strong bonding and also has a calming effect on a baby who is suffering from colic (massage gently over the tummy in a clockwise direction), restlessness, or the 'miseries'. Avoid the genitals and eyes when massaging and pay particular attention to the feet.

The All-Purpose Baby Oil may be used for any of the above conditions, for general skin care, to loosen cradle cap, and as an after-bath oil.

All-Purpose Baby Oil

80ml (2²⁄₃fl oz) sweet almond oil
20ml (²⁄₃fl oz) olive oil
5 drops chamomile oil
8 drops lavender oil

Mix all the oils together in a 100ml (3¹⁄₃fl oz) bottle. Shake well. Leave for 4 days to blend.

Healing Bottom Cream

1 cube (15g/¹⁄₂oz) beeswax
80g (2²⁄₃oz) lanolin
3 tablespoons olive oil
3 tablespoons almond oil
8 drops lavender oil
5 drops chamomile oil
10 drops tincture of benzoin

Gently melt the beeswax in a double boiler. Add the lanolin and melt. Mix the olive and almond oils and add slowly to the pan. Do not overheat. Take off the heat. Add the mixed lavender oil and tincture when the temperature is below 45°C (113°F). Stir until thoroughly incorporated but not set. Spoon into a pot.

For more comprehensive instructions on ointment-making, see page 11.

Nappy Rash Powder

Zinc oxide (obtainable from pharmacies) and lavender oil are wonderful for healing or preventing nappy rash. Overuse of powders is not recommended but a light dusting can help to keep little creases sweet and dry.

2 cups (300g/10oz) cornflour
2 tablespoons zinc oxide powder
20 drops lavender oil

Mix the cornflour and powder together very well. Add the oil 1 drop at a time. Stir constantly or lumps will form. Allow to stand for 4 days to blend. Shake occasionally to mix. Store in an airtight container.

BABIES FROM 2 TO 12 MONTHS

During this time the range of oils may be extended and the amount of oil increased but the amount of essential oils in the following remedies mustn't be exceeded.

Colic

🌺 Massage the abdomen gently using All-Purpose Baby Oil (see page 43), in a clockwise direction. Avoid the genitals.

Coughs and Colds

🌺 Combine 1 drop each of tea tree and lavender oils with 1 teaspoon vegetable oil. Pour in baby's bath and swoosh.
🌺 Place 3 drops of tea tree oil or lavender oil in a diffuser or a bowl of warm water under the cot.
🌺 Combine 3 drops each of tea tree and lavender oils with 1 tablespoon olive oil. Use as a chest massage.

Insect Bites

🌺 Add 1 drop lavender oil to 1 teaspoon bicarbonate of soda. Mix to a soft paste with a little water. Dab frequently on bites.

Teething

🌺 Combine 1 drop chamomile oil with 1 teaspoon almond oil. Massage baby's cheeks and jaw gently, avoiding the eye area.

CHILDREN OVER 12 MONTHS

Please take care not to exceed the recommended amount of oils. If your child has just graduated to the great age of 1-year-old it needs smaller dosages than an older child. If in doubt, use the dosages suggested in the previous section.

Your child is now entering a phase of life when legs and arms are usually covered in abrasions, cuts and bruises — worn like medals earned on a battle field! Make up the following Wound Wash for instant relief in emergencies.

Wound Wash

100ml (3⅓fl oz) purified water
10 drops lavender oil
10 drops geranium oil
10 drops tea tree oil

Mix all together in a 120ml (4fl oz) bottle. Shake well to blend. Leave for 4 days before use. Shake well before using. Pour a little of the lotion into a little bowl. Swab the wound until clean.

Antiseptic Ointment

This ointment may be used after the Wound Wash or at any time an antiseptic is needed on a wound.

1 cube (15g/½oz) beeswax
80g (2⅔oz) lanolin
3 tablespoons olive oil
3 tablespoons almond oil
20 drops lavender oil
20 drops tea tree oil
20 drops geranium oil
20 drops tincture of benzoin

Gently melt the beeswax in a double boiler. Add the lanolin and melt. Mix the olive and almond oils and add slowly to the pan. Do not overheat. Take off the heat. Add the mixed essential oils and tincture when the temperature is below 45°C (113°F). Stir until thoroughly incorporated but not set. Spoon into a pot.

For more comprehensive instructions on ointment-making, see page 11.

Bruises

🐝 Apply a bag of frozen peas or some ice blocks wrapped in cloth to the bruise as soon as the accident has occurred. Then do the following:

🐝 Mix 5 drops of either geranium oil or hyssop oil with 1 teaspoon vegetable oil. Massage very gently into the bruise.

Burns, Minor

🐝 Run cold water for up to 10 minutes over the burn. Apply a cold compress sprinkled with 2 drops of lavender oil.

Coughs and Colds

🐝 Combine 1–2 drops (depending on age) each of tea tree, lavender and rosemary oils to 1 teaspoon vegetable oil or full cream milk. Add to a warm bath.

🐝 Combine 2 drops each of tea tree, lavender and rosemary oils with 1 tablespoon vegetable oil. Massage onto the chest.

Cuts and Abrasions

🐝 Wash with Wound Wash (see opposite). Leave open to the air if possible but if severe, use Antiseptic Ointment (see opposite) and apply a dry dressing.

Earache

Earache must never be ignored. It can be a warning of very severe problems and infections which can result in permanent deafness or other major traumas. The infection may even reach the brain. If it persists for more than an hour or two, medical help needs to be obtained. The following treatment is for first aid of the problem and if the condition is mild (such as that caused by a cold) may clear it up very quickly.

🐝 Warm a teaspoon of virgin olive oil to blood heat only. Add 1 drop of tea tree oil to the warmed oil. Using a dropper, squeeze a few drops into the ear and plug the external opening of the ear with cotton wool.

Fevers

🐝 Children can run alarmingly high fevers very quickly. It's important to reduce the fever to reduce the chances of complications. Place cool (not icy cold) compresses on the forehead, replace often. Then do the following:

🐝 Add 2 drops each of tea tree, lavender and eucalyptus oils to a bowl of lukewarm water. Agitate to mix. Soak pieces of sheeting in the water, wring the cloth out and lay over the body of the child, avoiding the genitals. Change as soon as the sheeting warms up.

Chicken Pox

🐝 Add 20 drops of lavender oil (a drop at a time to prevent lumping) to 2 cups (360g/12oz) bicarbonate of soda. Mix 1 or 2 teaspoons with enough cold water to make a milky lotion. Use cotton wool balls to dab the lotion onto the itchy spots. Repeat as often as needed. Add bicarbonate of soda and 4 drops lavender oil to a warm bath to soothe the itching (has the added advantage of making the little patient calmer as well). Use this method for rubella (German measles) as well.

Measles

Measles is potentially a very serious disease and should never be treated lightly. It is best to confine the child during the contagious period.

🐝 Complete bed-rest is essential to help to avoid complications. Use the lotion as in Chicken Pox to treat the itchy rash. Give body sponges to reduce high temperature. Keep both the bedroom and the house sprayed with Anti-Plague Blend (see page 48).

Mumps

🐝 Bed rest is essential to avoid complications. The swollen glands under the ears may make the child very miserable as it becomes painful to eat or swallow. Massage the glands and the whole neck area gently with a blend of 2 drops lavender oil, 1 drop tea tree oil, 2 drops lemon oil and 1 tablespoon olive oil. Spray the bedroom and house with Anti-Plague Blend (see page 48).

HOME
AND
AWAY

~

The use of essential oils in the home can help to create an emotionally and physically healthy environment. The oils can perfume; deodorise; soothe or stimulate; act as disinfectants, insect repellents and ionisers.

Essential oils can be blended in such a way that the fragrances used in each area of your home will harmonise with each other. Every breath you, your family and friends take will enhance the quality of health, both physical and emotional.

THE LIVING AND DINING ROOM

Commercial disinfectants, air fresheners, carpet cleaners and other household cleaners are almost exclusively synthetic and can possibly do more harm than good to the people who use them (particularly to those of you who suffer from allergic reactions). The perfumes of these products clash with each other and they contain few therapeutic qualities other than a germicidal one in disinfectant, and even this function can be performed better by certain essential oils. The other advantage to be gained from the following suggestions and recipes is that they are environmentally friendly, the contents are largely natural, inexpensive and they work!

Air Sweetener

Create a happy, restful atmosphere in the living room and dining room with the following recipe. The aroma will give a cheerful welcome to your family and friends when they arrive home but will ensure that any bacteria and viruses they are carrying are not given a welcome.

Air sweetener blends may also be used in diffusers or a few drops placed on cold light globes (before switching on), radiators and other warm places.

1 teaspoon geranium oil
1 teaspoon bergamot oil
1 teaspoon lavender oil
1 teaspoon lemon oil
50 drops cinnamon oil
20 drops clove oil

Mix all the oils in a 25ml (about 1fl oz) bottle. Shake well. Leave for 4 days. Add 1 teaspoon of the oil blend to 50ml (1^2/$_3$fl oz) vodka or brandy in a spray bottle. Allow to dissolve and add 250ml (8fl oz) purified water. Shake well before use. Don't spray on polished furniture.

Anti-Plague Blend

There will be time when visitors or (heaven forbid!) the family have coughs, colds, flu or other contagious diseases. You can help protect yourself by using the following blend as a room spray. A few drops of the oil blend can be sprinkled on a tissue and kept in a pocket to take out and sniff from time to time.

1 teaspoon eucalyptus oil
1 teaspoon tea tree oil
1 teaspoon lavender oil
1 teaspoon pine oil
^{1}/$_2$ teaspoon thyme oil
^{1}/$_2$ teaspoon cinnamon or clove oil

Mix all the oils in a 25ml (about 1fl oz) bottle. Shake well. Leave for 4 days to blend. Add 1 teaspoon of the oil blend to 50ml (1^2/$_3$fl oz) vodka or brandy in a spray bottle. Allow to dissolve and add 250ml (8fl oz) purified water. Shake well before using. Don't spray directly onto polished furniture or it might leave a water stain.

Carpet Freshener

This powder is for all carpets but those of you with pets will particularly appreciate the deodorant and disinfectant properties.

2 cups (360g/12oz) bicarbonate of soda
4 tablespoons unperfumed talc
4 tablespoons borax
20 drops lavender oil
30 drops lemon oil
10 drops cinnamon oil
10 drops pine oil

Sift the dry ingredients together into a bowl. Mix the oils and add to the powders 1 drop at a time while stirring thoroughly. Store in a glass jar or a container with a sprinkler lid. Stir twice a day for 3 days before using. Sprinkle the mix lightly on the carpet. Leave overnight or for as long as possible before vacuuming.

OPPOSITE: *Credits: Porcelain dish from The Bay Tree. Tablemats from Linen and Lace of Balmain. Pomander from Lisa Milasas.*

Vacuum Cleaner

The oils used in the air sweetener or carpet powder may also be used to sprinkle in the bag of the vacuum cleaner to get rid of that horrible dusty smell which seems to build up.

Humidifying

The air in a heated sitting or dining room can get very dry, which in turn can dry the skin. Humidify and freshen the air by putting a few drops of essential oil blend in a small bowl of water and placing the bowl near the heat source.

Pomander

Pomanders are ornamental and practical. They last for years, slowly releasing into the air the perfume of oils and spices. Hang 1 or 2 in every room and refresh as often as needed with a few drops of appropriate oils.

I once made little pomanders from mandarins and kept them piled in a bowl in the sitting room — they looked and smelt absolutely lovely.

1. Choose firm, only just ripe citrus fruit; mandarins, oranges, lemons, grapefruit.

2. To prevent your fingers getting really sore, pierce holes first with a fine skewer and push the stems of whole cloves into the holes. Leave a clove-head width between each hole or else the cloves will be pushed out as the fruit shrinks.

3. I like to leave a narrow band free of cloves around and across the fruit. This creates an area to hold a ribbon for hanging the pomander. Alternatively you can bend a piece of fine wire, twice as long as the width of the fruit, into a hairpin shape and push it into the fruit before inserting the cloves.

4. Leave the loop of the wire protruding about ³/₄cm (¹/₄in). This can be used to thread ribbon through.

5. Make a mixture of ground cinnamon, nutmeg, cloves and ground orris root (purchase from a health food store).

6. Roll the prepared pomander into the spices until thickly coated. Wrap in tissue paper and leave in a warm place for 1–2 weeks.

7. Gently shake and tap the pomander to remove the surplus spices. Save all left over spice mixture in a tightly capped container ready for making your next pomander.

8. Sprinkle the pomander with a mixture of oils (choose those for the appropriate room). Allow to dry for 1 day before attaching ribbon.

Lemon Furniture Polish

This is a simple recipe but works very well. It gives a lovely gloss to the furniture and nourishes the wood as well.

50ml (1²/₃fl oz) olive oil
50ml (1²/₃fl oz) lemon juice
1 teaspoon lemon oil

Mix all the ingredients together. Bottle, shake until the mixture is completely blended. Take very little onto a soft cloth and apply with gusto to the woodwork! Use about once a fortnight only.

Scenting the Dining Table

A few drops of essential oil can be dropped on the underside of cloth tablemats or tablecloths where the heat of the plates will release the perfume. Choose perfumes which won't clash with or overpower the scent of the food. Citrus or spicy oils are most suitable.

Using an eye dropper, drip the same oil on the melted wax at the top of a lit candle. Don't drop oil on the flame!

Scented Writing Paper

Scented letters are a pleasure to receive and also make a gracious present. The perfume should reflect your personality or the personality of the recipient, but be careful not to make it overpowering.

Choose your favourite oil or your favourite blend from this book. Place a few drops of the oil on pieces of blotting paper or thin cloth and interleave them between the writing paper and envelopes. Leave the paper for a week or so for the scent to permeate.

BEDROOMS

ADULTS BEDROOMS

The bedroom is the place where adults spend about a third of their lives: sleeping, dreaming, talking and making love. It follows that it's particularly important that bedroom oil blends should be pleasing to the users.

Oils used in different areas of the bedroom should have the same type of fragrance. It would be disturbing to have a heavy, musky scent in competition with a citrus or floral blend. I give suggestions below for different types of bedroom oils; try making tiny amounts until you find what works best for you.

Romantic Nights

To create a romantic setting in the bedroom

2 teaspoons ylang-ylang oil
1 teaspoon lime oil
1 teaspoon petitgrain oil
40 drops palmarosa oil
30 drops patchouli oil
10 drops clove oil

Mix the oils together in a 25ml (about 1fl oz) bottle. Shake well to blend. Leave for at least 1 week to mature.

Sleep Time

This blend will help those of you who find that for no particular reason it's difficult to get to sleep

2 teaspoons chamomile oil
2 teaspoons lavender oil
40 drops marjoram oil
40 drops neroli oil or clary sage oil

Mix the oils together in a 25ml (about 1fl oz) bottle. Shake well to blend. Leave for at least 1 week to mature.

Mind Soother

This blend will help to chase away the anxieties and stresses of the day leaving your mind calm and ready for sleep

2 teaspoons bergamot oil
1 teaspoon lavender oil
40 drops melissa (lemon balm) oil or ylang-ylang oil
40 drops cedarwood oil
40 drops sandalwood oil or peppermint oil or juniper oil

Mix the oils in a 25ml (about 1fl oz) bottle. Shake well to blend. Leave for at least 1 week to mature.

The Feminine Bedroom

This blend is floral without being sickly

2 teaspoons rose geranium oil
1 teaspoon geranium oil
1 teaspoon orange oil
40 drops petitgrain oil
20 drops patchouli oil
20 drops cinnamon oil

Mix the oils together in a 25ml (about 1fl oz) bottle. Shake well to blend. Leave for at least 1 week to mature.

The Masculine Bedroom

Citrus and spice for the sensitive new-age man!

2 teaspoons bergamot oil
2 teaspoons lime oil
40 drops cinnamon oil
20 drops rosemary oil
20 drops black pepper oil

Mix the oils together in a 25ml (about 1fl oz) bottle. Shake well to blend. Leave for at least 1 week to mature.

To Use the Blends

❧ Air Spray: Add 1 teaspoon to 50ml (1⅔fl oz) vodka in a spray bottle of at least 300ml (10fl oz) capacity. Dissolve and add 250ml (8fl oz) purified water. Shake well before using.

❧ Bed: Put a couple of drops of oil on a cotton wool ball and tuck it under your pillow.

❧ Bed Linen: Add a few drops of your chosen blend to the rinsing water in the washing machine. Sprinkle a few drops on cotton wool balls and place them between linen in the drawers and cupboards.

❧ Woodwork: Add 3–4 drops to the water when you are washing the woodwork and windows in all the bedrooms.

Anti-Moth Blend

It's not always desirable to scent your wardrobe with the basic bedroom blends as the clothes will be impregnated with the perfume (unless you don't mind feeling sleepy or sensual at lunchtime!).

The following oils will keep the wardrobe and clothes drawers fresh and free from insects and moths, without interfering with your personal daytime perfume/aftershave or clashing with the bedroom blend.

1 teaspoon lavender oil

1 teaspoon rosemary oil

1 teaspoon lemon oil

Mix the oils together in a 15ml (½fl oz) bottle. Shake to blend. Leave for at least a week.

FOR WARDROBES: Sprinkle 2–3 drops of the blend on padded coat hangers. Add 2–3 drops of the blend to 2 cups (500ml/16fl oz) water when washing the inside of the wardrobe.

FOR DRAWERS: Sprinkle 2–3 drops of the blend on the lining paper of drawers containing underwear, woollens, sports clothes or put a few drops on several cotton wool balls and place between the clothes.

Smelly Shoes!

If you store shoes in the wardrobe it can create a less then pleasant ambience in the bedroom! Make up a quantity of Carpet Freshener (see page 48). Sprinkle a little in the shoes, shaking to spread it around, leave overnight and shake out in the morning. Alternatively (and I think better) pour a few spoons of the powder in the cut-off feet of a pair of stockings or pantyhose, tie a knot in the top and slip the sock in the shoes. These socks can be used for some time before more oils are needed to refresh them.

CHILDREN'S BEDROOMS

Children have their own stresses and worries: performance at school, peer pressure, bogeymen, over-stimulating movies. Try to make the last half hour before bedtime as calm as possible with maybe a warm bath, a glass of warm milk or herb tea, and a cuddle while reading a happy story.

Children are much more sensitive to essential oils than are adults and the blend for their bedrooms should be simple and restful. The following blend is suitable for all ages.

Children's Blend

1 teaspoon lavender oil

1 teaspoon chamomile oil

1 teaspoon geranium oil

Mix the oils together in a 15ml (½fl oz) bottle. Shake to blend. Leave for at least a week. Follow the suggestions for adults bedrooms (see page 51). A guide for safe quantities will be found in the Mother and Child section (see page 40).

OPPOSITE: *Credits: Flowers from Lisa Milasas. Potpourri bags from Linen and Lace of Balmain. Glass jars from Victoria's Old Charm Antiques.*

KITCHENS

Kitchens can be both a health and a nose hazard! Not only are many of the areas perfect breeding grounds for bacteria, but many of the smells are less than pleasant: boiled cabbage, fried or grilled meat and fish, rubbish bins and drains. The essential oils we use in the kitchen need to be powerful bacteria inhibitors but they should also smell fresh and clean.

Disinfectant Wash

1½ cups (300g/10oz) biodegradable,
phosphate-free laundry powder
1 litre (32fl oz) hot water
1 teaspoon lemon oil
1 teaspoon pine oil
20 drops cinnamon oil

Mix the laundry powder with the hot water. Stir gently until dissolved. Allow to cool until lukewarm. Mix the oils together and add slowly to the cooled liquid. Stir well to incorporate then bottle. Always invert the bottle before use to mix the oils and liquid.

All-Purpose Disinfectant Cleaner

This cleaner works hard to cut through grease and remove stains. It also acts as a powerful disinfectant. Use on working surfaces, tiles, painted woodwork. Avoid inhaling the ammonia fumes.

60g (2oz) bicarbonate of soda
2 litres (64fl oz) hot water
25ml (about 1fl oz) vinegar
3 teaspoons Bug Buster Blend (this page)
25ml (⅚fl oz) cloudy ammonia

Mix together the bicarbonate of soda and hot water. Allow to cool.

Combine the vinegar and Bug Buster Blend. Allow the oils to dissolve. Mix together with the ammonia. Mix very well then bottle. Shake well then decant some of the mixture into a spray bottle or pour directly onto a cloth to use.

Bug Buster Blend

25ml (about 1fl oz) lemon oil
3 teaspoons pine oil
1 teaspoon cinnamon oil
1 teaspoon tea tree oil

Mix the oils together in a 50ml (1⅔fl oz) bottle. Shake well to blend. Allow to stand for 4 days before using.

Trouble Spots

WORKING SURFACES: Use All-Purpose Disinfectant Cleaner.

CUPBOARDS: Add 8 drops Bug Buster Blend or 1–2 teaspoons of the Disinfectant Wash to 1 litre (32fl oz) warm water.

TEA TOWELS: Add 8 drops Bug Buster Blend and 1 teaspoon Disinfectant Wash to 2 litres (64fl oz) cold water as a pre-wash soak to sterilise. Leave overnight if possible.

DRAINS: To sweeten and disinfect, drop 4–6 drops of neat Bug Buster Blend down the drain after washing up.

RUBBISH BINS: Spray with All-Purpose Disinfectant Cleaner, wipe clean. Sprinkle 4 drops Bug Buster Blend into the bin or liner.

FLOORS: As for cupboards.

SINKS: Wash with 1 teaspoon All-Purpose Disinfectant Cleaner in 1 litre (32fl oz) warm water.

DISH WASHING: Use 1 teaspoon Disinfectant Wash in washing-up water.

DISHWASHERS: Add 2 drops Bug Buster Blend to dishwasher powder in compartment.

AIR SPRAY: Add 50 drops Bug Buster Blend to 50ml (1⅔fl oz) vinegar. Pour into a 300–400ml (10–13½fl oz) spray bottle. Add 250ml (8fl oz) water. Shake well before use.

OPPOSITE: *Credits: White liquid soap dispenser, bowl and huckerback face cloths from Linen and Lace of Balmain. Flowers from Australian Herb Suppliers. Nail brush, comb and shaving brush from The Body Shop.*

BATHROOMS

Bugs love bathrooms. Fungus growths and bugs love shower recesses. Many diseases (such as tinea) can be transmitted from person to person through the warm, moist bacteria- and fungus-laden floors of the shower recess.

No matter how often the shower is cleaned it can harbour these undesirable bugs unless the appropriate cleaning methods are used.

The oil blend for the bathroom contains both antibacterial and antifungal oils. Keep the cleaning materials in the bathroom and encourage the family to spray the shower and the air before leaving the room.

Bathroom Cleaner

This recipe is basically the same as All-Purpose Disinfectant Cleaner but contains different oils. It works wonderfully in the bathroom. It cleans wall and floor tiles, baths, showers, wash basins and their surrounds. If extra cleaning power is needed on stubborn stains use bicarbonate of soda as an abrasive in conjunction with the spray.

$\frac{1}{3}$ cup (60g/2oz) bicarbonate of soda
2 litres (64fl oz) hot water
25ml (about 1fl oz) vinegar
3 teaspoons Bathroom Oil Blend
25ml ($\frac{5}{6}$fl oz) cloudy ammonia

Mix together the bicarbonate of soda and hot water. Allow to cool. Mix together the vinegar and Bathroom Oil Blend. Allow the oils to dissolve. Mix all together with the ammonia. Mix very well.

Bottle. Decant some of the mixture into a spray bottle or pour directly onto a cloth. Shake mixture well before use.

Bathroom Oil Blend

3 teaspoons lemon oil
2 teaspoons bergamot oil
1 teaspoon citronella oil
2 teaspoons pine oil
1 teaspoon thyme oil
1 teaspoon tea tree oil

Mix the oils together in a 50ml ($1\frac{2}{3}$fl oz) bottle. Shake well to blend. Allow to stand for 4 days before using.

Trouble Spots

BATH AND WASHBASIN: Spray with Bathroom Cleaner, leave for a minute or two before wiping.
VANITY SURFACES: As above.
SHOWER: To disinfect the shower, add 1 teaspoon Bathroom Oil Blend to 100ml ($3\frac{1}{3}$fl oz) vinegar. Pour into a 300–400ml (10–$13\frac{1}{2}$fl oz) spray. Add 20ml ($\frac{2}{3}$fl oz) water. Shake to mix. Spray shower after use. Use Bathroom Cleaner as often as needed.
FLOORS AND TILES: Wash floors and tiles weekly with 2 teaspoons Disinfectant Wash (see page 54) in 1 litre (32fl oz) warm water.
AIR SPRAY: Add 50 drops Bathroom Oil Blend to 50ml ($1\frac{2}{3}$fl oz) vinegar. Pour into a 300–400ml (10–$13\frac{1}{2}$fl oz) spray bottle. Add 250ml (8fl oz) water. Shake well before use.

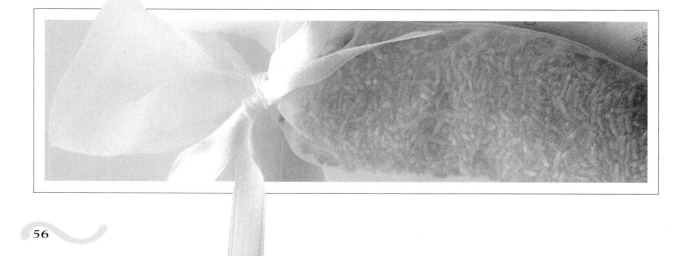

THE LAUNDRY

A laundry is often a multi-purpose room. It may be a repository for gardening and sports shoes, dirty-laundry baskets, mops, brooms and other cleaning equipment, beach towels and dog and cat beds. The smells which can build up and become interesting are often not the ones with which you want your home to be associated! The quality to be aimed at in the laundry is fresh and clean. The oils to use are the ones which are antibacterial, antifungal and deodorant.

The following blend will leave the wash fresh and lightly fragrant.

Laundry Blend

2 teaspoons lavender oil
1 teaspoon rosemary oil
1 teaspoon lemon oil
40 drops pine oil
40 drops lemon grass oil

Mix the oils together in a 25ml (about 1fl oz) bottle. Shake to blend. Leave for 4 days to mature.
PRE-SOAK: If there is contagious or infectious illness in the house, pre-soak bed linen, nightwear and any other appropriate garments in water to which you have added 10 drops of the Laundry Blend and 10 drops of eucalyptus oil.
WASHING: Add 4–5 drops of Laundry Blend to the final rinse water in the washing machine. Add 2 drops of this blend to rinse water if hand-washing.
TUMBLE DRYER: Put 2–3 drops Laundry Blend on a small piece of cloth and throw into the dryer.

Trouble Spots

FLOORS, CUPBOARDS AND SINKS: Use the Disinfectant Wash (see page 54).
AIR SPRAY: Spray the air, the inside of cupboards and baskets with Anti-Plague Blend (see page 48). This ensures a sweet and safe environment.
IRONING: Add 2 drops of the Laundry Blend (see above) to a spray bottle containing 300ml (10fl oz) purified water. Shake well before spraying If in doubt, test on the hem. Don't put essential oils directly into the iron.

THE TOILET

In the toilet area the two main concerns are bacteria and smells. An essential oil blend can take care of both these problems.

It's all very well telling children to wash their hands after going to the toilet, and as adults I'm sure that we automatically do this, but the very actions of pressing the flush button, opening the door and turning on a tap in the laundry or bathroom is going to spread bacteria from the, as yet, unwashed hands to many other people.

The use of an antibacterial/air-freshening spray means that the toilet seat, the flush button and the door handle are all being cleansed and the air sweetened every time the spray is used.

Toilet Blend

2 teaspoons tea tree oil
1 teaspoon lavender oil
1 teaspoon lemon oil
40 drops pine oil
40 drops lemon grass oil

Mix the oils together in a 25ml (about 1fl oz) bottle. Shake to blend. Leave for 4 days to mature. Add 1 teaspoon to 50ml (1⅔fl oz) vodka in a spray bottle. Allow to dissolve and add 1 cup (250ml/8fl oz) purified water.

Label clearly with the following instructions (or something similar): 'After using the toilet, please shake this bottle and spray up towards the ceiling to allow the mist to fall on toilet, door handle and this container.'

Trouble Spots

TOILET CLEANER: Sprinkle 10 drops of Toilet Blend in the toilet bowl after cleaning then scrub thoroughly.
TOILET SEATS AND WOODWORK: Use 1–2 teaspoons Disinfectant Wash (see page 54) and 5 drops eucalyptus or tea tree oil in 2 cups (500ml/16fl oz) water.
FLOORS: Use 2–3 teaspoons Disinfectant Wash (see page 54) and 10 drops eucalyptus oil in 2 litres (64fl oz) water.

THE WORKPLACE

These days many of us work both at home and away, not always from choice but often from economic necessity. This creates a situation where we are subjected to many physical, mental and emotional stresses.

How many of you feel stressed before you even arrive at work? You have often coped with making breakfast (or nagging others to do it), left the house tidy, organised the children, taken them to school (with World War III raging in the back seat) and then coped with rush hour traffic to get to the place where you are officially starting work! No wonder you feel permanently tired and edgy.

You need to make essential oils part of your everyday living as well as making sure that you are eating well, getting plenty of sleep, and learning some stress management techniques. Your life should be a joy, not a drag. If it's not then it's time to make changes and the first one can be to fill your life and your environment with essential oils.

Beat the Morning Blues Blend for Girls

2 teaspoons geranium oil
1 teaspoon lavender oil
2 teaspoons bergamot oil

Mix all the oils in a 25ml (about 1fl oz) bottle. Shake well then leave for 4 days to mature.

Add 10 drops of blend to 2 teaspoons sweet almond oil. Use as a body oil after your shower.

Put 2–3 drops on a wet flannel, squeeze to spread the oils and use to wipe over your body in the shower before drying yourself.

Put a couple of drops on a tissue to inhale while getting ready for work.

Wipe a few drops of the blend over the dashboard of the car.

Add 10 drops to a 50ml (1²⁄₃fl oz) atomiser of water. Shake then spray on the face, avoiding the eye area.

Beat the Morning Blues Blend for Blokes

2 teaspoons lemon oil
2 teaspoons rosemary oil
1 teaspoon cedarwood oil

Mix all the oils in a 25ml (about 1fl oz) bottle. Shake well. Leave for 4 days to mature.

Add 10 drops to 2 teaspoons sweet almond oil. Use as a body oil after the morning shower.

Put 2–3 drops on a wet flannel, squeeze to spread the oils and use to wipe over your body in the shower before drying yourself.

Add 20 drops to a small atomiser of water (about 50ml/1²⁄₃fl oz). Shake before use. Spray on your face as an after-shave, avoiding the eye area. It is a skin refresher and spirit lifter.

Put a couple of drops on a tissue to inhale while getting ready for work.

Wipe a few drops of the blend over the dashboard of the car.

Going to Work

Create a calm and positive atmosphere in the car by mixing equal amounts of peppermint and lavender oil in a small dropper bottle and storing in a small bag or box with some cotton wool balls. Use a drop or two on each cotton wool ball and tuck them on the dashboard, the rear window ledge, on top of the sun visors or anywhere out of the way where their calming yet uplifting qualities can be felt. If things are getting tense in spite of the oils, encourage everyone in the car (including you) to slowly lift their shoulders up to try to touch their ears while they breath in. Let the shoulders relax and drop as the breath comes out of the mouth in a long sigh. Kids find this good fun without realising that they are being de-stressed.

OPPOSITE: *Credits: White liquid soap dispenser, bowl and huckerback face cloths from Linen and Lace of Balmain. Flowers from Australian Herb Suppliers. Nail brush, comb and shaving brush from The Body Shop.*

AT THE WORKPLACE

Chances are that you work in a place that has air-conditioning, computers, synthetic carpets and veneered furniture. These are just a few of the hazards with which we are confronted every day. VDUs pose many health problems and we don't yet understand fully the effect the radiation and electricity emanating from the screen is having on users. We have all heard of the risks, such as Legionnaire's Disease, posed by inadequately maintained air-conditioning systems. Veneered furniture and the glue which holds them together can 'gas-off' if exposed to sunlight, causing allergies, headaches and possibly many more problems. All these things also increase the positive ion effect in the air and this can make you feel irritable, jumpy and miserable. Water helps to clear positive ions from the body so if you have an opportunity to have a quick shower in your lunch hour you will reap the benefits for the remainder of the day. Failing a shower, splash your hands, arms, face and neck with cool water.

The following oil blend will help to increase the negative ion effect. It has also been demonstrated that by using lemon oil aroma in the workplace, as many as half the errors are made by the VDU operators!

Oil Blend for VDU Users

This blend is usually enjoyed by everyone. It brings a fresh atmosphere into a stuffy office.

1 teaspoon cypress oil
1 teaspoon cedar oil
1 teaspoon pine oil
2 teaspoons lemon oil

Mix all the oils in a 25ml (about 1fl oz) bottle. Shake well. Leave for 4 days to mature. Put a few drops of the oil blend on a tissue and wipe over work surfaces. Add 10 drops oil blend to 1 teaspoon vodka in a small spray or atomiser. Leave for a day to dissolve. Fill with water and use to spray the air in the vicinity of your desk.

Keep a diffuser on your desk with a few drops of the oil blend floating on the water.

Afternoon Blend for Brain-Fatigue

It's 3 pm and your brain is totally fatigued. Keep a little bottle of the following blend in your pocket or drawer to chase away the cobwebs.

6 drops rosemary oil
3 drops lemon grass oil
2 drops basil oil
2 teaspoons sweet almond oil

Mix all the oils in a 10ml ($\frac{1}{3}$fl oz) bottle. Shake well. Leave for 4 days to blend. Place 1–2 drops on the pulse points of the wrist and throat, massage in and inhale the vapour.

Place a few drops on a tissue and inhale.

COLDS, INFLUENZA AND OTHER NASTIES

When you are suffering from any of these, please go to bed and stay there. Keep your germs to yourself. No one is indispensable and I get very cross when I see the advertisement for a cold cure in which the jingle urges people to 'soldier on'. This is downright antisocial as very soon many of the people with whom you come in contact each day will, in their turn, be struck down.

You can protect yourself from these airborne diseases by carrying some of the Anti-Plague Blend (see page 48) and using it in the ways suggested in that recipe.

OPPOSITE: *Credits: Desk set from Cane and Cottage. Potpourri and bag from Penny Lang. Small timber box from Linen and Lace of Balmain.*

PETS

Those of you who live with a dog or a cat will know just how much fun and pleasure these pets bring into our lives. Not only are they emotionally satisfying but physically they are a blessing to us, as it has been demonstrated that stroking of a pet can lower both stress and blood pressure levels.

Owning a pet helps children to learn to be gentle and responsible, and which child hasn't whispered secrets or troubles too private to be entrusted to an adult into the ear of a dog or cat.

Pets can suffer from ailments in the same way as their humans. Some of the treatments suggested below will ensure their happiness and comfort. If problems such as abscesses, coughs and cuts do not improve after several days of treatment, veterinary advice will be necessary.

Dogs and cats can encourage fleas to live in your house and these are certainly not beneficial to either pets or humans.

Fleas don't live on animals. They spend only short periods of time feeding on the animal and then they jump off to live and breed in carpets or animal bedding. If your home already has a flea problem it will probably take about 2 weeks of pretty conscientious work for the house and pet to become flea-free.

Flea-Ban Blend

You may double-up on any of the first 3 oils if you don't have them all, but don't increase the others.

1 teaspoon eucalyptus oil
1 teaspoon lavender oil
1 teaspoon citronella oil
1 teaspoon thyme oil
40 drops garlic oil
40 pennyroyal oil
1½ tablespoons vodka

Mix all the oils together in 50ml (1⅔fl oz) bottle. Leave for 4 days. See right for usage.

Carpets

Make up a batch of the Carpet Freshener (see page 48) substituting the oils in the recipe for an equal amount of Flea-Ban Blend (see this page). Sprinkle the carpets lightly with the powder every night for 2 weeks and vacuum each morning.

Flea Collars

Dogs and cats: Soak a cat or dog collar made from cloth in Flea-Ban Blend. Allow to dry before using on the animal. Repeat as often as necessary — probably every 3–4 weeks.

Pet Bedding

Wash cat and dog bedding in very hot water and add 1 teaspoon of Flea-Ban Blend to the last rinse. Hang the bedding in the sun every day until the flea problem is overcome — fleas hate sunlight.

Shampooing

For dogs, add 1–2 drops (depending on the size of the dog) of Flea-Ban Blend to the shampoo and a further 1–2 drops to the rinsing water.

Have you ever tried to bath a cat? Not a happy experience! If, however, your little mog doesn't mind water you can use 1 drop of Flea-Ban Blend in the shampoo and 1 drop in the rinse.

Between Shampoos

For dogs, add 4 drops of Flea-Ban Blend to 1 cup (250ml/8fl oz) warm water. Mix well. Soak a flannel in the water and wring out but leave enough moisture to dampen the dog's coat. Rub through the coat in a backwards direction avoiding the eyes and the genitals. Repeat daily.

Add 4 drops of Flea-Ban Blend to 1 teaspoon vegetable oil and use to massage into the fur behind the ears, the back of the neck and the end of the spine above the tail.

To treat cats, use as for dogs but using only half the amount of essential oils in each treatment.

OPPOSITE: *Credit: Special thanks to Grover the cat.*

Abscesses

To treat both cat and dogs, drip 1 drop of tea tree oil directly on the abscess. Repeat twice daily for 1 day, then once daily until healed.

Coughs and Colds

For both dogs and cats, add 12 drops eucalyptus oil, 10 drops lavender oil and 1 teaspoon olive oil to 50ml (1⅔fl oz) vodka. Leave for a day to dissolve and blend. Add 100ml (3⅓fl oz) water. Shake well to blend. Massage the lotion around the chest and throat up to the ears. Use the blend 2–3 times daily.

Cuts and Grazes

For both dogs and cats, add 1 drop thyme oil, 2 drops tea tree oil, 2 drops lavender oil to 2 cups (500ml/16fl oz) warm, boiled water. Bathe the wound with the lotion. If the injured part is a foot, immerse the whole foot in the liquid. Treat 2 hourly for 1 day then twice a day until healed.

BELOW: *Credits: Brush, comb, mirror and travel bag from The Body Shop. Potpourri bag from Linen and Lace of Balmain.*

Smelly Breath

Tartar build up on teeth is often a major cause of bad smelling breath in pets. If the tartar build up is very bad it may have to be removed by a veterinarian. Giving your dog an uncooked marrow bone to chew 2 or 3 times a week (or your cat some uncooked chicken wings), will give Towser a great deal of pleasure and will help to prevent tartar build-up.

The following tooth powder also helps to keep Towser's breath sweet.

Towser's Tooth Powder

1 drop clove oil
2 drops aniseed oil
1 drop orange oil
½ cup (90g/3oz) bicarbonate of soda

Drip the oils into the soda stirring well to incorporate. Sieve the mixture and pack into a small wide-mouthed jar. Dip a cotton wool ball into the powder. Rub firmly over the back and front of the teeth. Give the dog a drink of water to follow. Use once daily.

TRAVEL

Each year more and more people save money and plan excitedly for months in order to have their dream holiday either in their own country or overseas. A few simple precautions and a small but effective selection of essential oils helps to ensure that your holiday is as magical as you anticipated.

🌿 Always drink only bottled water.

🌿 Always clean your teeth with bottled water.

🌿 Always carry a small zip-top plastic bag containing tissues impregnated lightly with a few drops of thyme and cinnamon oils. Use them to wipe your hands before eating and to wipe toilet door handles, flush buttons and so on.

Travel Sickness/Nausea

I make up a 2 cup (500ml/16fl oz) bottle containing 2 teaspoons honey and 2 drops peppermint oil topped up with water. Then I use it as follows:

CHILDREN AGED 2–5 YEARS: 1 teaspoon mixture in ¼ cup (60ml/2fl oz) water.

CHILDREN AGED 5–12 YEARS: 2 teaspoons mixture in ¼ cup (60ml/2fl oz) water.

CHILDREN AGED 12–16 YEARS: ¼ cup (60ml/2fl oz) undiluted.

ADULTS: ½ cup (125ml/4fl oz) undiluted.

Flying High

The best way to carry this blend is in a spray bottle or failing this, in a little bottle with a screw top.

60 drops lavender oil
60 drops geranium oil
40 drops grapefruit oil
1 teaspoon vodka oil

Mix together in a 15ml (½fl oz) bottle. Shake well. Spray on a tissue and sniff as needed.

Carry a damp flannel in a plastic bag, spray very lightly with a little with Flying High blend (the equivalent of 1–2 drops) and use to wipe over the face and hands. If you are very nervous, wring the flannel out in hot water, spray as above and use as directed. The heat has a calming effect.

Toddler Tamer

Children can get very overexcited, tired and cranky when travelling. Make the following blend and use to massage their little arms and legs. Put a little on a tissue and encourage them to inhale, this will have a calming effect.

2 drops lavender oil
3 drops chamomile oil
1 tablespoon grape seed oil

Mix together in a 15ml (½fl oz) bottle. Shake well. Leave for 4 days to mature. This is for children over 2 years. For babies, see page 43.

Jet-Lag

To avoid jet-lag try to fit in with local time as soon as you reach your destination. Wait until the local bedtime before retiring and resist having a nap in the afternoon, even if you are very tired.

Come Alive

60 drops lavender oil
60 drops grapefruit oil
40 drops rosemary oil

Mix together in a 10ml (⅓fl oz) bottle. Shake well. Leave for 4 days to mature. Have a shower or bath on arrival. Add 10 drops of the Come Alive blend to a bath or, if showering, 1–2 drops on a hot moist flannel, well squeezed out and rubbed briskly over your whole body (avoiding eyes and genitals). These suggestions can also be used to recover from your trip when you return home.

Sleep Easy

60 drops lavender oil
60 drops geranium oil
60 drops chamomile oil

Make and use as for Come Alive blend (see above). Also, you could carry a 15ml (½fl oz) bottle almost full of the Basic Massage Oil (see page 38), and add 6 drops of the Sleep Easy blend. Either massage the oil all over your body after a shower or, ask someone to give you a massage!

GARDENS AND INSECTS

We are all now aware of the potential dangers of the many chemical pesticides and herbicides which are used to keep crops free from weeds and insect damage. Insects are attracted to plants largely by the smell; an example is the cabbage white butterfly being attracted to the brassica family, and carrot fly to carrots. By using herbs and herb oils in the garden we can mask the smell of vegetables in order to protect them from insects which would eat them. Other garden pests such as mice, slugs and snails can be deterred by using plants and oils whose scent they dislike.

Humans as well as plants can suffer in the garden, and what should be a pleasant and relaxing place to spend our leisure hours can be a place infested with flies, mosquitoes, midges and other insects that bite. Essential oils are very effective in deterring these creatures.

It's obvious that we need to take sensible precautions to prevent these nuisances from breeding in our gardens in the first place. Don't leave stagnant water in pots, buckets or other containers. Keep fish in garden ponds to eat mosquito larvae. Keep compost piles, grass clippings and other moist organic matter closely covered to prevent flies using the piles to breed in.

The essential oils will help to prevent (or cure) fungi, bacteria and viruses which attack plants.

Fungus, Bacteria and Virus Spray

8 drops chamomile oil
8 drops tea tree oil
50ml (1²/₃fl oz) paraffin oil
500ml (16fl oz) water

Mix the essential oils with the paraffin oil. Leave for 4 days. Add the water slowly, stirring constantly. Shake before use. Add 2 tablespoons mixture to 2 litres (64fl oz) water. Mix very well. Use to spray plants and seedlings.

General Anti-Pest Spray

This blend will prove effective against aphids, caterpillars, flies, moths and plant lice. It also helps to deter slugs and snails if used often.

4 drops peppermint oil
4 drops garlic oil
4 drops citronella oil
100ml (3¹/₃fl oz) paraffin oil
500ml (16fl oz) water

Make and use as for the Fungus, Bacteria and Virus Spray.

Anti-Mosquito Blend

This blend may be used on the body or in the outdoor eating area. Spray it in the air, on the table and, if using one, on the umbrella over the table. Pin ribbons to the edges of the umbrella or tablecloth and place a few drops of the Anti-Mosquito Blend on each piece. Mosquitoes *love* ankles and legs so either spray thoroughly under the table or put a bowl containing warm water and a few drops of the oil under the table where it won't get kicked.

1 teaspoon citronella oil
1 teaspoon lemon grass oil
2 teaspoons lavender oil
40 drops peppermint oil
40 drops thyme oil

Mix all the oils together in a 25ml (about 1fl oz) bottle. Leave for 1 week before using.
TO USE ON THE BODY: Put 40 drops of the Anti-Mosquito Blend in a 50ml (1²/₃fl oz) bottle and add 2 teaspoons vodka or witch hazel. Shake well. Leave for 1 day to dissolve. Fill with grape seed or almond oil. Shake well before rubbing onto exposed parts of the body.
TO USE AS AN OUTDOOR AIR/FURNITURE SPRAY: Put 1 teaspoon of the Anti-Mosquito Blend in a 300ml (10fl oz) spray bottle. Add 50ml (1²/₃fl oz) vinegar. Leave for 2 days to dissolve.

Add 1 cup (250ml/8fl oz) water. Leave for 4 days to mature. Shake well before use.

OPPOSITE: *Credit: Oil diffuser from The Body Shop.*

WELL
BEING

~

It's comforting and gratifying to know that you can deal with simple accidents or problems and, by swift and appropriate action, often prevent them from becoming worse.

It is beyond the scope of this book to deal with serious complaints and it must always be borne in mind that seemingly simple symptoms may mask serious ailments. Professional help needs to be sought if a condition persists or worsens.

Essential oils are highly concentrated and a few are very toxic. In view of this the oils are usually best employed externally or as inhalations. The oils are readily absorbed through the skin and then are carried around the body via the blood and lymphatic systems to influence internal organs and body systems.

THE ESSENTIAL OIL FIRST AID BOX

An essential oil first aid box is an invaluable addition to any home and car.

The following box contents are in addition to the usual bandages, sticking plasters, scissors and other contents of a first aid box.

2 empty dropper bottles
2 eye droppers
15ml ($\frac{1}{2}$fl oz) bottle almond oil
15ml ($\frac{1}{2}$fl oz) bottle brandy

Include essential oils as follows:

BLACK PEPPER: Antiseptic, pain-relieving and fever-reducing

CHAMOMILE: Antibacterial, antiseptic, anti-inflammatory, pain-relieving and calming

EUCALYPTUS: Anti-inflammatory, antiseptic, antiviral and pain-relieving

GERANIUM: Antiseptic, pain-relieving and astringent

LAVENDER: May be used undiluted. Antiseptic, antibiotic, antiviral and antidepressant

LEMON: Antiseptic, antibacterial, disinfectant.

PEPPERMINT: Antiseptic, antispasmodic, astringent, calming, anti-inflammatory

ROSEMARY: Antiseptic, astringent, pain-relieving and antispasmodic

TEA TREE: May be used undiluted. Powerfully antiseptic, antiviral, antibacterial, antifungal

The following list provides an indication of how much oil to use in any treatment. For descriptions of the treatments please refer to the section titled Blending and Storing Oils (see page 14).

ROOM SPRAY: See page 15.

BATHS: 4–10 drops essential oil (depending on age) in a full bath after the bath has been run.

FOMENTATIONS AND COMPRESSES: 5–10 drops essential oil (depending on age) in 100ml ($3\frac{1}{2}$fl oz) water.

GARGLE: 1 drop essential oil in 1 cup (250ml/8fl oz) water. Mix well. Gargle, spit and don't swallow.

MASSAGE OILS: 10–20 drops essential oil (depending on age) in 50ml (1⅔fl oz) oil.

MOUTHWASH: 4 drops in 25ml (about 1fl oz) brandy. Add 1 teaspoon to ¼ cup (60ml/2fl oz) warm water. Rinse mouth, but don't swallow.

INHALATIONS: 5–10 drops essential oil (depending on age) in 2–3 litres (64–96fl oz) hot water.

OINTMENTS: 30 drops essential oil to each 50g (1⅔oz) jar. (This may vary within recipes.)

WOUND WASH: 10–30 drops of essential oil (depending on age) in 100ml (3⅓fl oz) warm boiled water. Agitate to disperse.

AILMENTS

NOTE: Wherever possible use a blend of all the recommended oils.

Abrasions

ESSENTIAL OILS: Tea tree oil, lavender oil
TREATMENT: Wound wash using single or mixed oils. Repeat 2 hourly. Leave uncovered if possible. If a plaster is needed use one drop of either of the oils on the plaster.

Aches and Pains

ESSENTIAL OILS: Marjoram oil, black pepper oil, rosemary oil
TREATMENT: Use a mixture of the oils or use singly for massage and in baths.

Anaemia

ESSENTIAL OILS: Black pepper oil, lemon oil, peppermint oil
TREATMENT: Use singly or in combination for massage and in baths.

Arthritis

Osteoarthritis

ESSENTIAL OILS: Cedarwood oil, black pepper oil, rosemary oil
TREATMENT: Use singly or, for much better results, in combination for massage and baths.

Rheumatoid Arthritis

ESSENTIAL OILS: Rosemary oil, juniper oil, ginger oil
TREATMENT: As for osteoarthritis.

Athlete's Foot

ESSENTIAL OILS: Tea tree oil, myrrh oil, thyme oil
TREATMENT: For a foot bath, use 1 drop of each oil in a bowl (big enough for both feet) containing warm water. Add 2 drops of each oil to 1 teaspoon vegetable oil. Massage the whole foot and between the toes 4 times a day. Add 2 drops of each oil to 1 cup (150g/5oz) unperfumed talcum powder. Dust the feet before wearing shoes and socks. Pre-soak socks in Disinfectant Wash (see page 54) and wash them separately from the family laundry.

Bites and Stings

Bees

ESSENTIAL OILS: Chamomile oil, lavender oil
TREATMENT: Scrape the sting out sideways. Don't pull it out. Mix 1 drop chamomile oil, 1 drop lavender oil with 1 teaspoon bicarbonate of soda (counteracts the acidity of the sting) and enough water to make a soft paste. Apply to the painful area. Repeat hourly.

Dog Bites

ESSENTIAL OILS: Thyme oil, lavender oil, tea tree oil
TREATMENT: Wash the area immediately with Wound Wash (see page 44) using the above oils. Apple neat tea tree oil to the wound, cover with a light dressing. Go straight to hospital if the skin is broken as you may need a tetanus injection.

Mosquitoes, Gnats and Flies

ESSENTIAL OILS: Lavender oil
TREATMENT: Apply oil neat until relieved.

Snake

ESSENTIAL OILS: Lavender oil
TREATMENT: Try to identify snake. Flood wound with lavender oil. Bind limb firmly but not tightly with anything available. Keep patient calm and *still*. Seek medical help *immediately*.

Spiders

ESSENTIAL OILS: Lavender oil

TREATMENT: Add 5 drops oil to 1 teaspoon vinegar. Dab on bite every 4 hours. If you suspect the spider was of the poisonous variety, go straight to hospital dabbing wound constantly with neat lavender oil until hospital treatment begins.

Wasps

ESSENTIAL OILS: Lavender oil

TREATMENT: Add 4 drops lavender oil to 1 teaspoon vinegar. Dab on wound to counteract the alkaline poison of the sting and reduce pain and swelling. Repeat hourly.

Bleeding—External

ESSENTIAL OILS: Geranium oil, lemon oil, cypress oil

TREATMENT: Apply a cold compress containing the above oils. Bandage firmly, but not too tightly, in place.

Blisters

ESSENTIAL OILS: Lavender oil, tea tree oil

TREATMENT: Apply 2 drops neat of either of the above oils. Massage in gently. Don't break the blister.

Boils and Carbuncles

ESSENTIAL OILS: Bergamot oil, lavender oil, tea tree oil

TREATMENT: Wash 3 times daily with 2 drops bergamot oil and 2 drops lavender oil in 50ml (1⅔fl oz) warm, boiled water. Smooth on a mix of 5 drops tea tree oil to 1 teaspoon vegetable oil.

Breath Sweetener

ESSENTIAL OILS: Bergamot oil, peppermint oil, myrrh oil

TREATMENT: Make a mouthwash using the above oils. Use as often as needed.

Bronchitis

ESSENTIAL OILS: Benzoin oil, marjoram oil, eucalyptus oil

TREATMENT: Inhalation using a blend of the above oils. Massage chest with a blend of the oils.

Bruises

ESSENTIAL OILS: Geranium oil, clary sage oil, rosemary oil

TREATMENT: Hold a bag of frozen peas or iceblocks wrapped in cloth on the area for a few minutes. Massage with a blend of 6 drops of the above oils in 1 tablespoon vegetable oil.

Burns—Minor

ESSENTIAL OILS: Lavender oil

TREATMENT: Use ice-water compresses for 10 minutes. Gently pat on neat lavender oil. Cover with a dry dressing.

Catarrh

ESSENTIAL OILS: Peppermint oil, tea tree oil, rosemary oil

TREATMENT: Inhalation. Massage on chest and back.

Chilblains

ESSENTIAL OILS: Lemon oil, lavender oil, rosemary oil

TREATMENT: Massage initially with neat lavender oil. Make a blend of the above oils with vegetable oil and massage daily.

Cold Sores

ESSENTIAL OILS: Geranium oil or lavender oil

TREATMENT: Apply neat to sore.

Constipation

ESSENTIAL OILS: Black pepper oil, palmarosa oil
TREATMENT: Make a massage oil containing the above oils. Massage the abdomen daily in a clockwise direction.

Coughs and Colds

ESSENTIAL OILS: Eucalyptus oil, thyme oil, lemon oil, rosemary oil
TREATMENT: Use the above oils in the bath, massage and inhalation.

Cramps—Muscles

ESSENTIAL OILS: Lavender oil, black pepper oil, rosemary oil
TREATMENT: Blend above oils with vegetable oil for massage. Use 3 drops of each oil in a bath.

Cuts

ESSENTIAL OILS: Lavender oil, tea tree oil
TREATMENT: Compress to stop bleeding. Leave open to the air unless severe. If needed, put 2 drops of either oil on a dressing to cover.

Cystitis

ESSENTIAL OILS: Bergamot oil, benzoin oil, cedarwood oil
TREATMENT: 1 drop bergamot, 1 drop benzoin, 2 drops cedarwood in 2 teaspoons vegetable oil to massage over bladder. 3 drops of each in a hot bath.

Dermatitis

ESSENTIAL OILS: Chamomile oil, lavender oil, cedarwood oil
TREATMENT: 3 drops of each in bath. 2 drops of each oil in 2 teaspoons vegetable oil to be used as a topical application.

Diarrhoea

ESSENTIAL OILS: Peppermint oil
TREATMENT: See Travel Sickness/Nausea (page 65) for method to treat nausea and diarrhoea.

Earache

ESSENTIAL OILS: Tea tree oil, garlic oil
TREATMENT: 3 drops tea tree or garlic oil in 1 teaspoon olive oil warmed to blood heat (no hotter). Drip a few drops into the ear. Plug the external opening of the ear with cotton wool.

Eczema

ESSENTIAL OILS: Bergamot oil, lavender oil, chamomile oil
TREATMENT: As for Dermatitis.

Exhaustion

Physical

ESSENTIAL OILS: Lavender oil, peppermint oil, geranium oil
TREATMENT: Bath. Massage. Inhale scent of blended oils.

Nervous

ESSENTIAL OILS: Frankincense oil, peppermint oil, clary sage oil
TREATMENT: As for Physical.

Fainting

ESSENTIAL OILS: Marjoram oil or lavender oil
TREATMENT: Put a few drops of oil on a tissue and hold under the nose of the faint person or sniff directly from oil bottle.

Fatigue

ESSENTIAL OILS: Lemon oil, clary sage oil, lavender oil.
TREATMENT: As for Exhaustion.

Fever

ESSENTIAL OILS: Black pepper oil, lavender oil, peppermint oil
TREATMENT: Hot bath. Massage.

Fibrositis

ESSENTIAL OILS: Black pepper oil, peppermint oil, rosemary oil
TREATMENT: Massage.

Flu

ESSENTIAL OILS: Tea tree oil, peppermint oil, black pepper oil
TREATMENT: As for Fever.

Glandular Fever

ESSENTIAL OILS: Cypress oil, tea tree oil, lemon oil
TREATMENT: Bath. Massage neck and chest using 2 drops of each oil in 2 teaspoons olive oil.

Gum Infections

ESSENTIAL OILS: Tea tree oil, myrrh oil
TREATMENT: Mouthwash using either or both oils.

Haemorrhoids

ESSENTIAL OILS: Cypress oil, juniper oil, geranium oil
TREATMENT: Add 2 drops of each oil to half a bowl (large enough to sit in) of warm water. Agitate the water to disperse the oils. Sit in the water for 10–15 minutes. Follow with 1 drop of each oil in 1 tablespoon olive oil. Use to gently massage the haemorrhoids.

Hay Fever

ESSENTIAL OILS: Lavender oil, lemon oil, geranium oil, hyssop oil.
TREATMENT: Inhalation. Bath.

Headache and Migraine

Nerves

ESSENTIAL OILS: Lavender oil, marjoram oil
TREATMENT: Bath. Inhalation. Neck massage.

Gastric

ESSENTIAL OILS: Peppermint oil
TREATMENT: Massage the oil over stomach and abdomen. Inhalation. Bath.

Heartburn

ESSENTIAL OILS: Peppermint oil.
TREATMENT: See Travel Sickness/Nausea (page 65).

Hoarseness and Voice Loss

ESSENTIAL OILS: Cypress oil, sandalwood oil, thyme oil
TREATMENT: Inhalation. Massage throat.

Immune System Booster

ESSENTIAL OILS: Tea tree oil, garlic oil, eucalyptus oil, thyme oil
TREATMENT: Bath. Massage.

Indigestion

ESSENTIAL OILS: Peppermint oil, ginger oil
TREATMENT: See Travel Sickness/Nausea in Travel section (page 65).

Inflammation

ESSENTIAL OILS: Chamomile oil, lavender oil, sandalwood oil
TREATMENT: Cold compress.

Insomnia

ESSENTIAL OILS: Lemon balm oil, chamomile oil, lavender oil, marjoram oil
TREATMENT: Bath. Massage. Air spray.

Laryngitis

ESSENTIAL OILS: Benzoin oil, thyme oil, lavender oil
TREATMENT: Gargle. Throat massage.

Menopause

Hot Flushes

ESSENTIAL OILS: Clary sage oil, geranium oil, lime oil
TREATMENT: Bath. Massage. Air spray.

Depression

ESSENTIAL OILS: Ylang-ylang oil, clary sage oil, bergamot oil
TREATMENT: As for Hot Flushes.

Menstrual

Cramps

ESSENTIAL OILS: Bergamot oil, clary sage oil, cypress oil
TREATMENT: As for Hot Flushes.

Heavy loss

ESSENTIAL OILS: Cypress oil, rose oil, chamomile oil

TREATMENT: As for Hot Flushes.

Irregular

ESSENTIAL OILS: Clary sage oil, marjoram oil, chamomile oil
TREATMENT: As above.

Painful

ESSENTIAL OILS: Juniper oil, clary sage oil, marjoram oil
TREATMENT: As above.

Scanty

ESSENTIAL OILS: Myrrh oil, marjoram oil, clary sage oil
TREATMENT: As above.

Mouth Ulcers

ESSENTIAL OILS: Myrrh oil, clary sage oil
TREATMENT: Mouth wash.

Mucous

ESSENTIAL OILS: Benzoin oil, black pepper oil, tea tree oil
TREATMENT: Inhalation. Bath. Chest massage.

Nausea and Vomiting

ESSENTIAL OILS: Peppermint oil, lavender oil.
TREATMENT: See Travel Sickness/Nausea in Travel section (page 65).

Nervous Tension

ESSENTIAL OILS: Basil oil, marjoram oil, sandalwood oil.
TREATMENT: Bath. Massage. Air spray.

Pre-Menstrual Syndrome (PMS)

Nerves and Mood Swings

ESSENTIAL OILS: Chamomile oil, geranium oil, marjoram oil, rose oil
TREATMENT: As for Nervous Tension.

Water Retention

ESSENTIAL OILS: Fennel oil, juniper oil, rosemary oil

TREATMENT: Massage. Bath.

Psoriasis

ESSENTIAL OILS: Bergamot oil, lavender oil

TREATMENT: Facial steam (if problem on face). Bath. Add 6 drops mixed oils in 1 tablespoon sweet almond oil. Use to massage on troubled spots.

Rashes

ESSENTIAL OILS: Chamomile oil, lavender oil, tea tree oil

TREATMENT: Ointment. Baths. Compresses.

Rheumatism

ESSENTIAL OILS: Juniper oil, pine oil, rosemary oil

TREATMENT: Baths. Massage.

Ringworm and Scabies

ESSENTIAL OILS: Tea tree oil, myrrh oil, lavender oil

TREATMENT: Ointment. Tea tree applied neat.

Scalds—Minor

ESSENTIAL OILS: Lavender oil

TREATMENT: Apply oil direct onto scald.

Scar Tissue

ESSENTIAL OILS: Frankincense oil, lavender oil, sandalwood oil, myrrh oil

TREATMENT: 1 drop each essential oil in 2 teaspoons wheat germ oil, massage twice daily as long as needed.

Shock

ESSENTIAL OILS: Neroli oil, peppermint oil, mandarin oil, ylang-ylang oil

TREATMENT: Inhalation. Bath. Massage.

Sprains and Strains

ESSENTIAL OILS: Chamomile oil, lavender oil, rosemary oil

TREATMENT: Cold compress.

Stiffness of Muscles and Joints

ESSENTIAL OILS: Black pepper oil, lavender oil, rosemary oil

TREATMENT: Massage. Bath.

Sunburn

ESSENTIAL OILS: Lavender oil

TREATMENT: Bath. Gently smooth the massage oil on the sunburn.

Throat, Sore

ESSENTIAL OILS: Clary sage oil, geranium oil, lavender oil

TREATMENT: Inhalation. Gargle.

Tonsillitis

ESSENTIAL OILS: Bergamot oil, hyssop oil, thyme oil

TREATMENT: As for Sore Throat.

Varicose Veins

ESSENTIAL OILS: Bergamot oil, cypress oil, lemon oil

TREATMENT: Cold compress using 6 drops mixed essential oils in 2 drops of witch hazel.

Warts and Verrucae

ESSENTIAL OILS: Tea tree oil

TREATMENT: Drop neat oil onto wart or verrucae.

Wounds and Sores

ESSENTIAL OILS: Chamomile oil, lavender oil, tea tree oil

TREATMENT: Wound wash. Dry dressing with a few drops of lavender oil or tea tree oil on pad.

A-Z
OF
OILS

This is a description of some of the main essential oils. Buy one oil at a time as you can afford them until you have a basic collection of those most useful for your needs.

The most used oils are marked with an asterisk (*) and are good ones with which to begin your collection. They are some of the most generally useful and are among the least expensive. The oils marked will embrace a wide variety of applications, some of which are room sprays, inhalations, massage oils, skin treatments, ointments and perfumes.

In the following list of essential oils, you will notice that an oil's quality (i.e. Yin or Yang) and its Ruling Planet: (e.g. Saturn) are mentioned.

Yin and Yang are oriental terms which signify the duality of everything in life. Male and female, night and day, sickness and health, summer and winter — all things have this duality but nothing is entirely either Yin or Yang.

All the essential oils carry these characteristics of Yin and Yang. It must be remembered that as with all things, essential oils are never completely either Yin or Yang but one or the other is usually predominant.

Basil
Ocimum basilicum

NOTE: Top
QUALITY: Yang becoming Yin
RULING PLANET: Mars
PARTS USED: Flowering tops and leaves
PERFUME: Refreshing, uplifting and green
BLENDS WITH: Bergamot, geranium and hyssop
PHYSICAL USES: Appetite stimulant, antiseptic, bronchitis, earache, gastroenteritis, hiccups, migraine, hair tonic.
MENTAL/EMOTIONAL: Stimulates and clears the brain and intellect, aids concentration. Reaches into our conscious mind to help us to choose the right path or make the right decision. Lifts depression, eases hysteria, insomnia, anxiety.
MAGICAL PROPERTIES: The perfume of basil is the one to inhale if you want to attract money. It needn't be the pure essential oil, the fresh or dried leaf, crushed to release the oil is fine. As you hold and smell the plant, visualise yourself having lots of money: in the bank, in your wallet, in a purse or pocket, under the mattress or wherever!
CAUTION: Never use basil internally and only in minute quantities externally. Never use during pregnancy.

BENZOIN*
Styrax benzoin

NOTE: Base
QUALITY: Yang
RULING PLANET: Sun
PARTS USED: Resin exuded from damaged bark
PERFUME: Pleasant, warm, balsamic
BLENDS WITH: Rose, sandalwood
PHYSICAL USES: Fixative for other perfumes and oils Antiseptic, helps to preserve ointments, creams and lotions. Mildly stimulant. Cystitis, vaginal discharges. Inhalation for bronchitis, coughs and colds. Fungus infections of the skin, skin irritations, cracked, dry skin.
MENTAL/EMOTIONAL: Gently but powerfully works its way through to our subconscious to release hidden resistances and tensions and reveal new aspects of our natures. It comforts and eases our conscious mind when we are grief-stricken, lonely, stressed or mentally exhausted. Benzoin is a communicator and will help you to connect with people in difficult or uncomfortable situations.
MAGICAL PROPERTIES: Extra powerful protector especially if mixed with cumin. As you inhale the scent of either the oils or the crushed resin and seeds, visualise anyone or anything you want to protect being surrounded by a barrier to anything which might harm them.
CAUTION: Only simple tincture of benzoin should be used (see page 94).

BERGAMOT*
Citrus bergamia

NOTE: Top
QUALITY: Yang
RULING PLANET: Mars
PARTS USED: Rind of a non-edible citrus fruit grown mainly in Southern Italy. Not to be confused with the herb Bergamot *Monarda didyma.*
PERFUME: Fresh, sweet and citrus-like
BLENDS WITH: Cypress, jasmine, lavender, neroli
PHYSICAL USES: Used to impart the traditional flavour to Earl Grey tea. Antiseptic. Cold sores, thrush, pruritis. Cystitis and other urinary infections. Skin conditions such as acne, eczema, psoriasis and ulcers.
MENTAL/EMOTIONAL: A grounding oil which brings you joyfully into the 'here and now'. Lightens depression and nerves by calming and lifting the spirit.
MAGICAL PROPERTIES: Use a few drops of the oil in a diffuser or room spray to ensure the happiness and prosperity of the home and the people who live in it.
CAUTION: The oil can cause irritation if used on a sensitive skin. It is also phototoxic — do not use on exposed skin during long exposure to sunlight or pigmentation may occur.

CEDARWOOD
Juniperus virginiana; Cedrus atlantica

NOTE: Base
QUALITY: Yang
RULING PLANET: Sun
PARTS USED: Wood and leaves
PERFUME: Aromatic and warm
BLENDS WITH: Cypress, juniper and rose
PHYSICAL USES: Antiseptic Arthritis and rheumatism. Acne and skin diseases. Urinary tract problems. Bronchitis and catarrh. Cosmetics. Insect repellent.
MENTAL/EMOTIONAL: Soothes the nervously over-excitable. Softens and mellows those with selfish, unyielding, stiff-necked attitudes. Allows us to release mental strain and stress. Gently soothes and aids those with depression and insomnia.
MAGICAL PROPERTIES: Use as incense or in a room spray or diffuser before meditation to increase spirituality.
CAUTION: Not to be used internally. Not to be used at all during pregnancy. An irritant to some sensitive skins.

Basil

CHAMOMILE*
Anthemis nobilis,
Matricaria
chamomilla

NOTE: Middle
QUALITY: Yin
RULING PLANET: Moon
PARTS USED: Flowers
PERFUME: Refreshing, pleasant and apple-like
BLENDS WITH: Geranium, lavender, patchouli, rose
PHYSICAL USES: Flatulence, diarrhoea and stomach complaints. Irregular and painful periods. Toothache, teething pains. Skin antiseptic and anti-inflammatory. Stimulates cell growth.
MENTAL/EMOTIONAL: Soothes the nervously over-excitable. Relieves mental strain and stress. Relieves depression and insomnia.
MAGICAL PROPERTIES: Inhale the scent before meditation to promote a feeling of calm.

CINNAMON
Cinnamomum
zeylanicum

NOTE: Middle
QUALITY: Yang
RULING PLANET: Sun
PARTS USED: Bark, twigs, leaves
PERFUME: Fragrant, spicy — similar to melissa
PHYSICAL USES: Antiseptic, antibacterial. Viral diseases such as influenza. Rheumatism. Circulatory stimulant. Promotes appetite and helps digestion. Insect repellent.
MENTAL/EMOTIONAL: Increases awareness of spirituality
MAGICAL PROPERTIES: Use the crushed bark or the essential oil to increase psychic ability and to bring wealth.
CAUTION: Do not use in large quantities. Do not use neat on skin as it will irritate.

CLARY SAGE*
Salvia sclarea

NOTE: Middle
QUALITY: Yang
RULING PLANET: Mercury
PARTS USED: Whole herb
PERFUME: Intoxicating, sweet, floral and fixative
BLENDS WITH: Cedarwood, geranium, juniper, lavender, sandalwood
PHYSICAL USES: Menstrual pain and irregularity. Sore throat. Antiseptic. Skin care for mature, dry skin. Reputed to have aphrodisiac properties.
MENTAL/EMOTIONAL: Clary sage has the ability to expand our range of experiences both emotional and creative. Allays stress, anxiety and depression and in doing so gives us the clarity and opportunity to deal with the cause. In small doses it can alleviate hysteria and paranoia.
MAGICAL PROPERTIES: If sniffed will produce a state of euphoria but this should not be indulged in for more than a few minutes, or too often, as abuse will result in very severe headaches.
CAUTION: Large doses cause severe headache and poisoning. Not to be used in pregnancy.

CLOVE *

Eugenia carophyllus

NOTE: Middle
RULING PLANET: Jupiter
PARTS USED: Flower buds
PERFUME: Pungent and spicy
PHYSICAL USES: Antiseptic. Often used in toothpastes. Digestive. Analgesic for toothache, arthritis and rheumatism. Insect repellent.
MENTAL/EMOTIONAL: Combines endurance and strength with assertiveness and determination. Dispels guilt over money. Why choose the rest when you can have the best? Reaches deep into the recesses of the mind to stimulate the memory.
MAGICAL PROPERTIES: Traditionally used as part of an exorcism ceremony and also as an assertiveness strengthener.
CAUTION: Must never be used neat or in high concentration on skin.

CYPRESS

Cupressus sempervirens

NOTE: Middle
QUALITY: Yin
RULING PLANET: Saturn
PARTS USED: Leaves, twigs
PERFUME: Clean and woody
BLENDS WITH: Juniper, lavender, pine, rosemary, sandalwood
PHYSICAL USES: Menopausal problems. Circulatory stimulant for cold hands and feet, varicose veins. Coughs, laryngitis, colds. Oily skin, broken capillaries.
MENTAL/EMOTIONAL: Eases the pain of loss or separation from loved ones and allows us to 'let go' with love. Lightens the burden of gloominess and introspection.
MAGICAL PROPERTIES: Another of the protective herbs used to create a safe home or personal environment.

EUCALYPTUS *

Eucalyptus globulus and other species

NOTE: Top
QUALITY: Yin
RULING PLANET: Saturn
PARTS USED: Fresh leaves and twigs
PERFUME: Clean, camphoric and cleansing
BLENDS WITH: Lavender, rosemary, pine
PHYSICAL USES: One of the most powerful natural antiseptics. Asthma, colds, coughs, bronchitis and sinusitis. Throat infections. Wounds and sores. Aches and pains. Mosquito deterrent. Removes many stains and grease marks from clothes.
MENTAL/EMOTIONAL: Brain cleanser. Crystallises the mind like a gust of rain and wind cleansing the dust from the trees in the forest.
MAGICAL PROPERTIES: Spray or diffuse the oil to dispel anger or unwanted psychic energies from the home. Use in the same way during a purification ceremony when there has been physical or mental illness.

FENNEL

Foeniculum vulgare

NOTE: Middle

QUALITY: Yang

RULING PLANET: Mercury

PARTS USED: Seeds

PERFUME: Similar to aniseed

BLENDS WITH: Frankincense, geranium, lavender, rosemary, rose

PHYSICAL USES: Liver cleanser and digestive problems from indigestion to constipation. Menopausal irregularities. Obesity (affects hormones), cellulite, fluid retention.

MENTAL/EMOTIONAL: Cheers and consoles when we have insecurities regarding our physical appearance. Gives the courage to make changes.

MAGICAL PROPERTIES: For purification ceremonies, add to other oils with the same properties.

CAUTION: Phototoxic. Not to be used on skin before exposure to sunlight. Not to be used internally, in pregnancy or in epilepsy.

Fennel

FRANKINCENSE

Boswellia thurifera, B. carterii

NOTE: Base

QUALITY: Yang

RULING PLANET: Sun

PARTS USED: Bark

PERFUME: Spicy and sweet

BLENDS WITH: Basil, citrus, cypress, lavender, patchouli, pine, sandalwood

PHYSICAL USES: Perfumery as a fixative. Expectorant for catarrhal conditions and asthma. Uterine tonic particularly during labour. Urinary tract infections such as cystitis. Cleanses wounds and ulcers. Helps keep wrinkles at bay!

MENTAL/EMOTIONAL: Calms and quietens those people who nervously gush and babble. While we should cherish the past we need to live in the present. This ancient and spiritual oil enables us to 'be here now'.

MAGICAL PROPERTIES: One of the most powerful oils for deepening meditation and for making us aware that the spiritual world is constantly and strongly present in our more obvious physical world.

CAUTION: Can be very irritating if used directly on the skin.

GERANIUM*

Pelargonium graveolens

NOTE: Middle

QUALITY: Yin

RULING PLANET: Venus

PARTS USED: Leaves, flowers, stems

PERFUME: Sweet, refreshing and relaxing

BLENDS WITH: Most. Harmonises and balances other scents.

PHYSICAL USES: Antiseptic. Skin problems such as dermatitis and eczema. Urinary disorders. Throat and mouth infections. Stimulates oily, sluggish skin.

MENTAL/EMOTIONAL: The gentle bringer of grace and harmony. An uplifting and calming perfume, particularly useful for women and especially for those moving through menopause.

MAGICAL PROPERTIES: Traditionally used to encourage fertility; to ward off psychic attack; and for protection and dispelling of negative energy.

GINGER
Zingiber officinalis

NOTE: Middle

QUALITY: Yang

RULING PLANET: Mars

PARTS USED: Root

PERFUME: Rich and spicy

BLENDS WITH: Lavender, orange, petitgrain

PHYSICAL USES: Appetite stimulant; digestive; antiseptic; antispasmodic; tonic; reduces fever; eases sore throats; reduces flatulence; prevents travel sickness. Externally ginger oil may be used in analgesic rubs to ease the pain of rheumatism and arthritis.

MENTAL/EMOTIONAL: Sexually arousing; builds physical courage and confidence in ones capabilities to survive. Creates a store of vibrant energy.

MAGICAL PROPERTIES: The root is traditionally worn to attract money, power and sexual attractiveness.

HYSSOP
Hyssopus officinalis

NOTE: Middle

QUALITY: Yang

RULING PLANET: Jupiter

PARTS USED: Leaves, flowers

PERFUME: Difficult to describe; a combination of camphor and spice

BLENDS WITH: Citrus, geranium, lavender, rosemary, sage

PHYSICAL USES: Raises and lowers blood pressure. Expectorant, useful for asthma, coughs, emphysema and catarrh. Digestive, eases flatulence, mild constipation and gastroenteritis. Cardiovascular tonic. Used in high-class perfumes and liqueurs.

MENTAL/EMOTIONAL: Clears the mind, quickness and clarity. Lessens nervous tension and brings relaxation.

MAGICAL PROPERTIES: Used for centuries as a sacred herb.

CAUTION: Toxic in large doses. Never to be used by epileptics or in pregnancy.

JASMINE
Jasminum officinale, J. grandiflorum

NOTE: Base

QUALITY: Yang

RULING PLANET: Jupiter

PARTS USED: Flowers

PERFUME: One of the most expensive. Exotic, sensual, relaxing

BLENDS WITH: Most especially rose and citrus

PHYSICAL USES: Menstrual and uterine pain. Respiratory system, coughs, catarrh, hoarseness, laryngitis. Dry irritated skin, dermatitis.

MENTAL/EMOTIONAL: Uplifting and transforming, it will raise and lighten the listless spirit. The scent of jasmine is best known for its aphrodisiac qualities. It has the ability to stimulate our responses to create sexual desire.

MAGICAL PROPERTIES: Use the oil or fresh flowers during visualisations concerning any aspects of love: spiritual, sexual, parental, friendship. If you are having problems in any of these areas, breath in the perfume as you visualise a situation where you are giving and receiving unconditional affection and love. Jasmine is also a powerful protector and can be used alone or in conjunction with other protective oils and herbs.

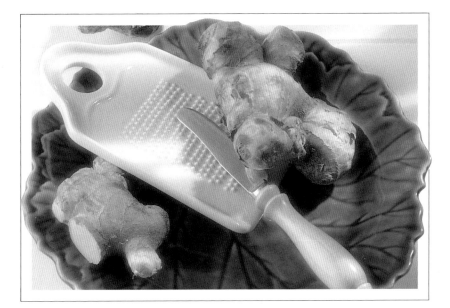

JUNIPER
Juniperus communis

NOTE: Middle
QUALITY: Yang
RULING PLANET: Jupiter
PARTS USED: Berries
PERFUME: Sharp and stimulating
BLENDS WITH: Citrus, cypress, lavender, pine
PHYSICAL USES: Purifies air in sick rooms. Relieves urine retention. Haemorrhoids (well diluted). Gout. Acne, dermatitis, eczema. Muscular pain.
MENTAL/EMOTIONAL: This vital oil will dispel the stress created by leading a busy people-filled life. It creates a calm, clear flow to the brain and psyche.
MAGICAL PROPERTIES: A good oil to purify a new home which has a spiritually or psychically uncomfortable feeling.
CAUTION: Not to be used in pregnancy.

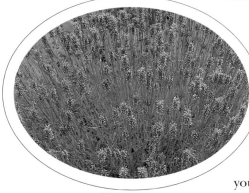

Lavender

LAVENDER*
Lavandula angustifolia/officinalis

NOTE: Middle
QUALITY: Yang
RULING PLANET: Mercury
PARTS USED: Flowering tops, leaves
PERFUME: Fresh, clean, floral and soft
BLENDS WITH: Most other oils
PHYSICAL USES: May be used undiluted. If you can only afford one oil, choose lavender, it is safe, versatile and gentle. Antiseptic and antibacterial. Stimulates cell growth. Eases problems with the digestive, respiratory and urinary systems. Rectifies menstrual irregularity. Eases the pains of rheumatism, sprains and aches and pains. Acne, eczema, psoriasis. Burns, sunburn, boils, insect bites. Insect repellent.
MENTAL/EMOTIONAL: Beautiful lavender is the great leveller. It can create calm and order from mental chaos to harmonise and balance every aspect of our bodies and minds.
MAGICAL PROPERTIES: Use the oil in visualisations to strengthen the physical body and conscious mind. See yourself, clear-headed and in perfect, glowing health.

LEMON*
Citrus limonum

NOTE: Top
QUALITY: Yin
RULING PLANET: Moon
PARTS USED: Rind of fruit
PERFUME: Sharp and fresh
BLENDS WITH: Grapefruit, lavender, orange, rosemary
PHYSICAL USES: Digestive problems. Gall bladder and liver tonic. Fever. Water purifier. Lymphatic tonic. Antiseptic.
MENTAL/EMOTIONAL: Clears the mind of sluggishness and apathy. Brightens the outlook leaving the mind alert and clear.
MAGICAL PROPERTIES: Inhale the perfume and visualise yourself revitalised, energetic and clear-headed.

Lemon

PENNYROYAL
Mentha pulegium

NOTE: Top
QUALITY: Yang
RULING PLANET: Mercury
PARTS USED: Leaves
PERFUME: Warm, pungent and minty
PHYSICAL USES: Uterine tonic. Hysteria and nervous exhaustion. Nausea, flatulence, indigestion. Liver and spleen tonic. Insect repellent.
MENTAL/EMOTIONAL: Nerve strengthener.
MAGICAL PROPERTIES: Use in mixtures for purifying a new home or clearing unpleasant vibrations left by negative or hostile people.
CAUTION: Never to be used internally. Absolutely never to be used in pregnancy.

Peppermint

PEPPERMINT*
Mentha piperita

NOTE: Middle
QUALITY: Yang
RULING PLANET: Mercury
PARTS USED: Leaves
PERFUME: Refreshing, cooling/warming
BLENDS WITH: Benzoin, lavender, rosemary
PHYSICAL USES: Indigestion, flatulence, diarrhoea, nausea and vomiting. Antispasmodic, stomach cramps, asthma, coughs and bronchitis. Analgesic, neuralgia, rheumatic pain.
MENTAL/EMOTIONAL: Stimulant, promotes mental clarity and rouses the conscious mind. Encourages positivity and enables one to overcome negative thoughts. Relieves the symptoms of shock, hysteria and palpitations.
MAGICAL PROPERTIES: Use in rituals and visualisations to invoke the power of healing. The healing can be for either places or people.
CAUTION: Use in smaller quantities than other oils — 1% is plenty. Peppermint oil should never be used by pregnant women.

PETITGRAIN*
Citrus aurantium

This is distilled from the same tree as Neroli but the oil is extracted from the leaves and twigs whereas neroli is from the flowers. It can be used as a less expensive substitute for neroli but the perfume is not as subtle or sweet and the therapeutic properties not as profound.
NOTE: Middle
QUALITY: Yang
RULING PLANET: Sun
PARTS USED: Leaves and twigs of the bitter orange
PERFUME: Sweet with sharper under notes of citrus
BLENDS WITH: As for neroli
PHYSICAL USES: Useful in perfume mixes as a middle note moderator balancing top and base notes. Deodorant. Hair rinse.
MENTAL/EMOTIONAL: Changes the feeling of wanting to be alone to one of sociability. Clears the conscious mind and leaves it bright, cheerful and aware.
MAGICAL PROPERTIES: Traditionally used to ward off physical threats. Make a little bag, either green or blue, and into it put a few leaves of pennyroyal and sage, a few pine needles and cumin seeds and a small piece of benzoin. Sprinkle with 3–4 drops of petitgrain. Tie the neck of the bag with a gold cord or ribbon and visualise yourself safe from all evils. Carry the bag on your person and repeat the visualisation as often as needed.

PINE*
Pinus sylvestris

NOTE: Middle/base
QUALITY: Yang
RULING PLANET: Mars
PARTS USED: Needles, twigs and cones
PERFUME: Resinous and clean
BLENDS WITH: Cedarwood, eucalyptus, rosemary, sage, tea tree
PHYSICAL USES: Powerful antiseptic. Respiratory system, asthma, catarrh, sinusitis, sore throat, flu. Urinary infections, cystitis. Arthritis, rheumatism, gout, neuralgia.
MENTAL/EMOTIONAL: Pine comforts and strengthens us when we are feeling unworthy or unsure of ourselves. It tells us that we are unique and helps us to tap into our inner power.
MAGICAL PROPERTIES: Powerfully protective and energising. Use in any ritual which involves protection, cleansing or asking for money.

Rosemary

ROSE
Rosa centifolia, R. damascena, R. gallica

NOTE: Base
QUALITY: Yin
RULING PLANET: Venus
PARTS USED: Petals
PERFUME: Queen of perfumes, sensual and romantic
BLENDS WITH: Most
PHYSICAL USES: Antiseptic. Good for all skins, tonic and soothing. Female problems such as menstrual irregularity, leucorrhoea. Stimulates secretion of bile. Nausea, vomiting. Stimulates circulation.
MENTAL/EMOTIONAL: Rose is the Queen, through whom we can reach our highest spiritual aspirations. Sensual but never sensuous it teaches us to be loving, caring and compassionate both to ourselves and others. Warmly relaxing, this oil reduces tensions and lifts our spirits from gloomy introspection and depression.
MAGICAL PROPERTIES: Love, love, love. Any ritual which is involved with love will be enhanced and strengthened if rose petals or oil are used.

ROSEMARY*
Rosmarinus officinalis

NOTE: Middle
QUALITY: Yang
RULING PLANET: Sun
PARTS USED: Leaves
PERFUME: Sharp and penetrating
BLENDS WITH: Basil, bergamot, citrus, lavender, peppermint
PHYSICAL USES: Powerful antiseptic, antibacterial, astringent, antispasmodic, analgesic. Asthma, coughs, colds, flu, bronchitis. Headache, neuralgia. Liver and gall bladder. Wounds, burns. Digestive, flatulence, constipation, diarrhoea.
MENTAL/EMOTIONAL: No sentiment but a warm heart. Here is the practical teacher, giving strength and power to our thinking and clearing wooliness from our minds.
MAGICAL PROPERTIES: For protection, love and purification. When you are working towards an exam, a diffuser or room spray containing rosemary oil will clear the mind and strengthen the memory. Sniff the oil and do a visualisation of yourself easily and confidently taking and passing the examination.
CAUTION: Not to be used in pregnancy or epilepsy.

SANDALWOOD*
Santalum album

NOTE: Base

QUALITY: Yang

RULING PLANET: Uranus

PARTS USED: Heart wood of trees at least 25 years old

PERFUME: Woody, spicy, oriental

BLENDS WITH: Most, but especially benzoin, rose, neroli, petitgrain

PHYSICAL USES: Antiseptic. Urinary system cleanser, cystitis. Antispasmodic. Respiratory infections, catarrh, cough, sore throat. Digestive, colic, nausea. All skins, acne, inflamed.

MENTAL/EMOTIONAL: Traditionally used in temples and for meditation, sandalwood is spiritual and uplifting. It can help us to move deeper into meditation by allaying the fears which are sometimes present when we begin to explore the deep, secret regions of our psyche. Sandalwood is also recognised as one of the few true aphrodisiacs and can help to promote sexuality in those who suffer from impotence or frigidity.

MAGICAL PROPERTIES: Sandalwood has been used for centuries in religious ceremonies of many kinds. It is the best oil to use in incense, diffuser or as a room spray when preparing a room for meditation. The perfume helps us to reach our spirituality and very deep levels in our subconscious mind.

TEA TREE*
Melaleuca alternifolia and M. leucodendron

The king of healing oils. Ranked as the Number 2 antiseptic oil (thyme being the first). It is reputed to be 100 times stronger than carbolic acid and has the advantage of being safer to use than thyme. Keep several bottles in the house and car.

NOTE: Top

PARTS USED: Leaves

PERFUME: Resinous, slightly musty

PHYSICAL USES: May be used undiluted on skin. Strong disinfectant: Antiviral, antifungal, antibacterial, antiseptic. Urinary tract infections and cystitis. Vaginal trichomonas, candida, thrush, herpes. Abscesses, athlete's foot, corns, warts, ringworm. Respiratory infections, coughs, bronchitits, colds. Cold sores. Mouth ulcers, gingivitis, bad breath, tonsillitis. Acne, boils, burns, sunburn.

MENTAL/EMOTIONAL: All the properties give confidence.

MAGICAL PROPERTIES: Use the leaves or oil of this plant in any rituals where protection or cleansing is being requested.

Tea Tree

THYME*
Thymus vulgaris and chemotype linalol

'Linalol' thyme oil contains very little of toxic phenols and is safer to use, particularly for the skin; during pregnancy and for children.

NOTE: Middle

QUALITY: Yang

PARTS USED: Flowers, doubly distilled

PERFUME: Warmly, sweetly pungent

BLENDS WITH: Bergamot, petitgrain, rosemary

PHYSICAL USES: The most antiseptic oil. Antispasmodic. Stimulates the immune system. Respiratory, asthma, bronchitis, catarrh, coughs, croup, emphysema, whooping cough. Skin, boils, wounds, sores. Cold sores, thrush, leucorrhoea. Stimulating, low blood pressure. Digestive, flatulence. Head colds, flu, headaches, sinusitis. Diuretic—removes uric acid in arthritis, gout. Deodorant.

MENTAL/EMOTIONAL: Thyme gives courage. It strengthens the will and dispels unfounded fears in those who are depleted through either illness or overactive imaginations.

MAGICAL PROPERTIES: For those of you who suffer from recurring nightmares, a pillow containing a little dried thyme would be useful — don't use too much or the scent might keep you awake.

CAUTION: A very powerful oil, use only $\frac{1}{2}$–1%. Never use neat. Never use during pregnancy.

YLANG-YLANG*
Cananga odorata

NOTE: Base
QUALITY: Yin
RULING PLANET: Venus
PARTS USED: Flowers
PERFUME: Sweet, sensual, exotic
BLENDS WITH: Jasmine, neroli, rose, sandalwood. Makes a useful fixative for perfumes
PHYSICAL USES: Tonic effect on the scalp. Aphrodisiac. High blood pressure and palpitations, rapid and irregular heart beat.
MENTAL/EMOTIONAL: Tranquilising, antidepressant and calming. This oil can create a calming environment in which to tackle unpleasant jobs or issues.
MAGICAL PROPERTIES: The calmer and creator of peace and love. Use this oil in all visualisations or other rituals connected with the dispelling of anger, negativity, fear or frigidity.

Thyme

Brief descriptions follow of other useful oils which are included in recipes.

ANISEED
Pimpinella anisum

PARTS USED: Seeds
PERFUME: Warm and spicy
MAIN USES: Indigestion, coughs bronchitis, catarrh.
CAUTION: Avoid where there is an inflammatory or allergic skin conditions. Narcotic in large doses.

CITRONELLA
Cymbopogon nardus

PARTS USED: All parts
PERFUME: Clean and lemony
MAIN USES: Insecticide. Deodorant. Perfumery. Headaches, migraine and neuralgia. Antiseptic. Rheumatic pain.
CAUTION: Avoid during pregnancy.

GARLIC
Allium sativum

PARTS USED: Bulb
MAIN USES: Respiratory tract infections; skin eruptions; high blood pressure; ringworm; viral and bacterial diseases.

GRAPEFRUIT
Citrus X paradisi

PARTS USED: Fresh peel
PERFUME: Fresh sweet citrus aroma
MAIN USES: Oily skin. Skin toner. Cellulitis, obesity. Muscle stiffness. Chills, colds Depression, nervous exhaustion.

LEMON GRASS
Cymbopogon citratus

PARTS USED: Leaves
PERFUME: Green-citrus scent
MAIN USES: Antiperspirant. Insect repellent. Headaches and nervous exhaustion.

LIME
Citrus aurantifolia

PARTS USED: Peel of unripe fruit. Whole fruit
PERFUME: Fresh, sweet and lemony
MAIN USES: See Lemon.

MANDARIN
Citrus reticulata

PARTS USED: Peel
PERFUME: Intense. Deliciously sweet, citrus-floral
MAIN USES: Oily skin. Stretch marks and scars. Obesity. Insomnia, nervous tension.

PALMAROSA
Cymbopogon martinii

PARTS USED: Whole plant
PERFUME: Sweet, rose-like and floral
BLENDS WITH: Geranium, cedar and sandalwood
MAIN USES: Intestinal infections. Invaluable for all types of treatments for the skin as a moisturiser and cell regenerator.

GLOSSARY

Acid/Alkaline: Skin has an acid mantle with a pH which ranges between 5.5 and 6.2. This mild acidity protects the skin from invading bacteria. Most soaps leave the skin in an alkaline condition. The skin will readjust the balance but, depending on other factors, this may take from $\frac{1}{2}$ to 2 hours during which time the skin is at risk. The use of a mildly acidic tonic will restore the balance immediately.

Alcohols: Ethanol alcohol is a 95% proof alcohol and is used, at various dilutions, for making tinctures, astringents and for dissolving essential oils. In Australia and Britain it's not possible to buy this alcohol without a licence. Some pharmacists will sell small amounts if they know you as a responsible person. If you can't find a supply, it's perfectly all right (albeit very expensive) to use the highest proof alcohol that you can find. Vodka, brandy, gin and other similar drinks are suitable. There is a Polish vodka which is 80% proof.

Allergen: Any substance which creates an allergic reaction. There isn't a substance on this earth which won't cause an allergic reaction on someone but some substances are more likely than others to cause a problem. If you are allergy-prone or have a sensitive skin it would be wise to patch test doubtful substances before including them in products and using them on your body.

To make a patch test, add 1 drop of the oil you wish to test to 1 teaspoon vegetable oil, massage a little inside your elbow. Cover with a sticking plaster and leave for 24 hours. If there is no soreness, itching or redness you can safely go ahead and use the oil. You can test other substances in the same way.

Allspice (Pimenta officinalis): The dried berry of the pimento, an evergreen tree up to 13 metres tall. Allspice has some anaesthetic effect which makes it useful in healing ointments and therapeutic massage oils. The lovely spicy smell makes it especially appropriate to use in hair rinses, tonics, colognes and baths for men. It provides a spicy note in potpourris and sachets.

Almond Oil: See Fixed Oils.

Analgesic: A substance which is applied to lessen pain by exerting a nerve-numbing effect.

Anodyne: Pain-easing and soothing.

Antifungal: A substance which inhibits the growth of fungus.

Antiseptic: An agent which inhibits the growth of bacteria on living tissue and prevents sepsis. Tea tree oil is a powerful antiseptic.

Astringent: An agent which has the power to contract tissues. Witch hazel extract is an example.

Avocado Oil: see Fixed oils.

Baby oil: See Fixed Oils.

Beeswax: A wax, secreted by bees, which forms the cell walls of the honeycomb. Beeswax is an ideal wax to use in ointments and creams.

Bicarbonate of Soda: Otherwise known as baking soda or sodium bicarbonate. Mixed with salt it makes an excellent tooth cleaner. It eases pain quickly if made into a paste with water or vinegar and essential oils and applied to stings or ant bites.

Borax: A mineral collected from the shores of alkaline lakes. Borax is mildly alkaline and softening and may be used effectively in many cosmetic products. Borax shouldn't be used internally, on broken skin, or for babies.

Bran: The husk of grains such as oats, barley and wheat. Bran may be used as a substitute for, or mixed with, oats as a water softener in recipes for bath bags. It is also a useful ingredient in facial scrubs.

Bran is a very valuable addition to our food intake as it acts as a natural laxative if taken in moderate quantities regularly.

Castor Oil: See Fixed oils.

Compress: A method of applying heat, cold, stimulation, moisture or the healing properties of various agents to areas of the body. For methods of preparation see page 11.

Deodorant: An agent which either disguises or inhibits body odours.

Digestive: An agent which helps digestion. An example is peppermint oil.

Disinfectant: A substance which destroys bacteria and so helps to prevent disease.

Distilled Water: See Water.

Emollient: An agent used to soothe external inflammation or dryness.

Emulsion: A mixture of oil and water which, when combined, doesn't separate. See page 11.

Enfleurage: A method of extracting essential oil from petals of flowers, in particular, jasmine and tuberose (see page 12).

Epsom Salts (magnesium sulphate): A mineral salt originally obtained from the springs at Epsom in Surrey. Epsom salts is an excellent additive to baths, where it eases tired bodies and aching muscles, and to foot baths for those times when your feet are killing you.

Essence: A mixture of oil and alcohol; for the purpose of this book an essence is a mixture of 15ml ($^{1}/_{2}$fl oz) essential oil with 1 cup (250 ml/8fl oz) high-proof vodka or brandy. This is a 6% solution.

Examples of essences which could be used in the kitchen would be peppermint and vanilla essence. Essences have many uses such as in perfume, deodorants and house sprays.

Fixative: Usually a base note essential oil used to fix the more fleeting perfumes of top and middle notes.

Fixed Oils: Natural, usually non-volatile oils, occurring in the seeds, kernels, beans, etc. of plants and extracted by presses, chemicals or heat. Fixed oils are fats which are liquid at room temperature (not to be confused with the aromatic or essential oils; for these oils, see page 6).

There is considerable dispute regarding the benefits of cold-pressed versus chemically extracted oils. I am assured by a very reputable pharmaceutical chemist that the solvent used to dissolve oils from their base seed, fruit etc. is evaporated off at a low temperature and that no trace remains in the oil at the end of the process, also that the nutritional content remains the same. He

added further that on analysis it is impossible to differentiate between the oils treated chemically or by cold-pressing.

In her book, *Health on your Plate*, Janet Pleshette presents a totally different perspective, she says that the oil-bearing materials go through 15 separate processes involving chemical solvents, caustic soda and deodorants which remove lecithin, vitamin E and minerals. She goes on to state that 'The heat used in refining oils can reach about 235°C (455°F). The oils are often held at this high level for several hours and it is this prolonged heat which is damaging'. She also states 'We have seen that refining oils destroys most of their nutrients'.

Cold-pressed oils are perceived by many as being preferable because there has been no chemical or heat applied in the extraction process. The name 'cold-pressed' is a misnomer as the pressure used in the press causes the heat to rise to 120°C (248°F), however, this is far less than the refining process.

The ultimate choice of oils must be yours, dictated by your preferences and (up to a point) your purse.

Oils are classified as:

(a) Non-drying: Non-drying oils contain mainly oleic acid glycerides, very little linoleic or linolenic acids. They remain liquid at normal temperatures and do not form a film when exposed to oxygen. These are the oils which are most suitable for dry and normal skins and are the main ones to use in massage oils.

(b) Semi-Drying: These oils contain more linoleic and linolenic acids, dry slowly to a soft film when exposed to oxygen and are suitable for dry to normal skins. These oils should be used in small quantities in massage oils.

(c) Drying Oils: Drying oils are high in linoleic and linolenic acids, low in oleic acids and dry quite quickly to a tough, elastic film when exposed to oxygen. These oils are often added to paints to shorten the drying time.

Drying oils are not advised for inclusion in massage oils as they would form a film on the skin but may be included in creams and lotions as the combination of ingredients during emulsification alters the character of the oil.

It's wise to keep all oils in the refrigerator as this helps to delay oxidisation/rancidity for as long as possible. The addition of the contents of vitamin E capsules also helps to prevent rancidity as vitamin E is a natural antioxidant.

THE FIXED OILS

ALMOND OIL, BITTER: The delicious scent of this oil, expressed from the kernel of the bitter almond (Prunis amygdalus), makes it a popular addition to perfumes and soaps. The unprocessed oil contains prussic acid which by law must be removed before the oil is offered for sale.

ALMOND OIL, SWEET: A fine, emollient, non-drying oil expressed from the kernel of the sweet almond (Prunis communis dulcis). An excellent oil to use in creams, lotions and massage oils for dry, normal and combination skins.

APRICOT KERNEL OIL: A pale yellow oil obtained from the kernel of apricot seeds. The oil contains minerals and vitamins. A light, non-drying/semi-drying oil which is suitable for all skins especially mature, sensitive and dry.

AVOCADO OIL: A beautiful thick, green semi-drying oil. According to Mrs Leyel in her book Herbal Delights - 'Avocado Pear oil ... used as a cosmetic, has greater powers of penetration than any other vegetable oil ... it conveys vitamins and nourishment to the glands that lie beneath the skin'. It contains vitamins A, D, E and K, is rich, nourishing and is invaluable in moisture creams and lotions, particularly for sensitive and sunburnt skins. The vitamin E content helps to preserve other oils in blends. Because of its thick consistency, use no more than 5–10% in oil blends.

CANOLA OIL: Canola seed is modified rape seed. Rape seed oil has been under a cloud due to the presence of eructic acid which, when eaten in large quantities showed a fat accumulation in the heart muscle of animals. Canola was bred to be genetically low in eructic acid. This process was first carried out in Canada, hence the first three letters in the name.

Canola is a non-drying oil which is excellent in massage oils and in creams and lotions for dry and normal skins. It is also good for cooking as it is light and has little flavour of its own. If you like the taste of butter but don't want to eat so much saturated fat, you could beat some canola oil into softened butter. This will give a spreadable consistency, less saturated fat and the benefits of mono-unsaturated fat. It still has the same number of calories!

CASTOR OIL: A rich non-drying oil pressed from the seeds of the castor oil plant (Ricinis communis). (The seeds themselves are very poisonous). An invaluable oil for use in hair conditioners, as hot packs on sore muscles and to draw splinters which are deeply embedded in the flesh. It is richly emollient if included in small quantities in night creams and soaps.

Note: Not recommended for internal use as it can cause severe 'griping' pains.

COCONUT OIL: Coconut oil is a semi-solid saturated fat extracted from the white meat of the coconut. It is a wonderful lubricant and moisturiser for delicate eye and throat areas. If used very discreetly it conditions and gives a shine to hair.

It's sometimes possible to buy saponified coconut oil to make shampoos and bath foams. If refrigerated it remains solid but liquefies easily when at room temperature.

COPHA: An Australian product made from hydro-genated coconut oil, copha is much cheaper than coconut oil. Use in creams, ointments and soaps.

CORN OIL: A good cosmetic oil but Jeanne Rose in her book The Herbal Body Book comments 'I cannot recommend its use since a large percentage of the pesticides and fungicides that are employed in this country (the US) are used on corn.' I haven't been able to establish if the situation is the same in other countries so it becomes a case of 'let the buyer beware'. Note that corn oil goes rancid more quickly than most other oils.

EVENING PRIMROSE OIL: Expressed from the seeds of evening primrose (Oenothera biennis), a tall, weedy herb with yellow flowers. The oil taken internally has many therapeutic uses such as PMS, menopausal problems, heart disease, skin conditions, multiple sclerosis and much more. It is a soothing, healing oil when added to creams and blends to help heal eczema, psoriasis and other inflammatory skin conditions. Use 10% in blends.

GRAPE SEED OIL: As the name suggests, this oil is pressed from grape seeds. It's a fine, semi-drying, polyunsaturated oil which makes it suitable for most skins except for the very oily. It is a very good basic carrier oil as it is light, clear and has no smell. Add 5–10% wheat germ oil to prevent rancidity.

HAZELNUT OIL: A fine yellow oil pressed from the kernel of the hazel nut. This oil contains vitamins, minerals and protein and is good for all skins. If you are feeling reckless and want to make a superlative cream or oil, 100% hazelnut oil may be used but as this oil is becoming increasingly difficult to buy you may want to use it sparingly.

JOJOBA OIL: A yellow waxy oil pressed from the bean of the desert plant Simmondsia chinensis. Contains a waxy substance similar to collagen which gives skin a silky smooth feel. Useful for acne, eczema, hair conditioner, inflamed skin, psoriasis. Penetrates deeply. Use 10% in blends.

MINERAL/PARAFFIN OIL (BABY OIL): Not much good for anyone and certainly not for babies! It is used extensively by cosmetic companies in cleansers, moisture creams and lotions because it's cheap, hypoallergenic and is completely inert, which gives it indefinite shelf life. If used alone it remains on the surface of the skin but once incorporated in an emulsion it is absorbed into the skin in the same way as other oils. The only advantage is that it doesn't go rancid.

Many books on natural cosmetics state that mineral oil 'leaches the vitamins from the skin'. This is not strictly accurate. All oils used both internally and externally will collect fat soluble vitamins (A, D, E, K) as they travel through the body, but natural oils are then absorbed through the intestines, hence the vitamins aren't lost. Mineral oil isn't absorbed into the intestinal wall and the oil is excreted, along with the vitamins.

OLIVE OIL: A rich non-drying oil expressed from ripe olives. It is one of my favourites and I use cold-pressed Extra Virgin which is from the first pressing and is very green and aromatic. Some people don't like the smell, they could try one of the lighter oils. Olive oil is too rich for oily skins but is excellent for massage oils, creams, soaps and lotions for dry and normal skins. This oil contains 80% oleic acid.

PALM OIL: A non-drying oil expressed from the kernel of the fruit of the palm tree. Palm oil has similar properties to coconut oil. It is used commercially in the manufacture of soap.

PEACH KERNEL OIL: Same as Apricot kernel oil.

PEANUT OIL (ARACHIS OIL): Peanut oil is a pale yellow non-drying oil with a faint, pleasant nutty odour and bland nutty taste. It contains protein, vitamins and minerals. For dry and normal skins.

SAFFLOWER OIL: A semi-drying, polyunsaturated oil obtained from safflower seeds. Contains protein, vitamins and minerals. It is an excellent 'all-rounder', good to balance other oils in preparations and may be used, mixed with other oils, in massage oils, soaps, moisture creams and lotions and bath oils. Safflower oil needs refrigeration.

SESAME OIL: A semi-drying oil expressed from ripe sesame seeds. Contains protein, vitamins, minerals, lecithin. It is useful in all moisturising creams and lotions. Sesame oil absorbs ultraviolet rays so may be used in suntanning preparations.

SOY OIL: An unsaturated drying oil expressed from soya beans. Contains protein, vitamins and minerals. It can be used in cleansing creams, moisturisers, massage and bath oils.

SUNFLOWER OIL: A semi-drying oil which may be used even by those with oily skin. Use on throats and around eyes where there are few oil glands and thin skin. Contains vitamins and minerals.

VEGETABLE OIL: This term to covers a mixture of oils. The problems with using vegetable oil in preparations is that there may be a mixture of canola, sunflower, safflower, soy or others — all good oils but with different properties. You would not know the quantities of the oils in the mixture.

WHEAT GERM OIL: A nourishing, fine, healing oil. The vitamin E content makes it useful for most skins, especially dry, prematurely aged skin, or for eczema and psoriasis. Good in anti-stretch mark blends. In creams and lotions, massage oils and soaps, 10% of the oil is a valuable addition.

Fomentation: The use of hot wet cloths to ease pain and reduce inflammation.

Fuller's Earth: This is a fine, naturally occurring mineral clay which ranges in colour from white to grey-green. It may be used as an oil-absorbing, cleansing and thickening agent in soaps, face packs and masks (mainly for oily skins). The absorbent property makes it a useful dry shampoo for oily hair or as a foot powder for sweaty feet! The clay was used in the textile industry to cleanse and thicken cloth or to 'full' woollen fabric — hence the name.

Glycerine: Glycerine is a natural substance present in animal and vegetable fats. It is usually obtained as a by-product of soap making. It is syrupy in consistency, colourless, odourless, sticky and sweet. If used in small proportions in lotions, creams and toners it acts as an antibacterial, softener, lubricant and humectant (holding moisture in the skin). If more than 20% is used in any recipe it will have the opposite effect and draw water from the skin. Adding a little glycerine to colognes gives a soft feeling to an after-shower splash.

Glycerine acts as a preservative, but in order to be effective, it needs to be present as 20% of the total content, which would be far too much for most recipes, but even a small amount will help to preserve to some degree particularly if it is combined with a 4% tincture of benzoin.

Humectant: A substance which has the capacity for attracting and holding moisture in the skin. Glycerine and honey are humectants.

Hyper-Pigmentation: Excessive skin pigmentation caused by over-exposure to sun or use of plants or oils which cause photo-sensitivity. Bergamot oil is one.

Kaolin: A very fine white clay powder with great absorption properties. Kaolin in powder form is used commercially for making porcelain, soap, paint and paper. Cosmetically it can be used as a base for masks and packs, particularly for oily/combination skins as it will absorb the grease from the skin.

Lanolin, Anhydrous: Also known as 'woolfat'. This is a sticky yellow grease obtained by boiling the shorn wool of sheep. I stopped using lanolin for some time because of the many chemicals which were poured on the sheep's back.

The new methods of treating sheep have resulted in purer lanolin, but there will still be a pesticide residue in the wool fat if the sheep have grazed on pasture which has been treated with organophosphates, as these are deposited in the fat of both animals and humans and are cumulative.

Much work is apparently being done on producing biodegradable pesticides which wouldn't present the risks to health that the present ones pose (unless you happen to be a ladybird, frog, praying mantis etc! I still can't come to terms with the use of pesticides, herbicides etc. on such a widespread scale).

I now feel that health wise, lanolin is probably a safer choice than petroleum jelly but I would recommend that nursing mothers could try substituting cocoa butter and coconut oil in nipple creams instead of lanolin.

Lanolin is often sold as hydrous lanolin, which means that water has been beaten into the lanolin to make it more spreadable. All the recipes in this book contain anhydrous (no water added) lanolin, unless otherwise stated. Allergen.

Liquid Paraffin: See Mineral Oil.

Moisturiser: A liquid, lotion, cream or other agent which adds moisture or helps it to retain moisture.

Oats (Avena sativa): If you have porridge left over from breakfast, save it until bath time, fasten it in cheesecloth and dump it in your (or the baby's) bath. It will soften the water, soothe and smooth skin and get rid of itches. Use the bag as a washcloth, there's no need to use soap unless you are really grimy. There are many other ways to use oats: in masks, scrubs, soaps and hand preparations.

Orris (Iris florentina) Root: Orris is the violet-scented dried, two-year-old rhizome of the Florentine iris which has a bearded purple flower. The powdered root is used as a fixative in potpourris and perfumes. It is used in soap-making and in body and tooth powders and pastes. Many people are allergic to orris root, so test before using. Allergen.

Photo-Sensitivity: A condition where the skin becomes oversensitive to light after the application of certain substances. The skin may develop rashes, swellings, redness or hyperpigmentation.

Rosewater: A scented water made from rose petals or rose oil. Triple rosewater (which may be bought from pharmacies) is prepared by the distillation of fresh blooms of Rosa Damascena.

To use, add 1 part rose water to 2 parts purified water. The resulting rosewater can be used in cleansing creams, toners, moisture lotions and as a toilet water.

Salve: A soothing, softening and healing ointment.

Sebum: Fatty secretion which lubricates hair and skin.

Solubalizer: I have just discovered this wonderful plant-derived product which is produced by Sunspirit in Byron Bay, New South Wales, Australia.

This syrupy liquid has very little smell and is used as an emulsifier to disperse essential oils into water. Use 1 drop Solubalizer to each 4 drops of essential oil. When added to water or oil and agitated, an emulsion is created and the oils are completely dissolved into the carrier liquid.

If using Solubalizer, there is no need to use alcohol to dissolve the oils. For instance, in the Air Sweetener recipe on page 48, the 50ml (1⅔fl oz) vodka or brandy would be replaced by 20 drops of Solubalizer.

Storax (Styrax) (Liquidambar orientalis): A balsam formed in damaged bark of the tree. The bark is collected, peeled and boiled to obtain raw storax which is then purified to a syrupy delicately perfumed substance.

Storax is used in perfumes as a fixative and in soaps, creams and lotions for the scent. Unfortunately it's becoming increasingly difficult to buy.

Talcum Powder: A mixture of various chalks which are milled until very fine. It's most important to use only sterilised talcum as earth borne bacteria, such as tetanus, may be contained in unsterilised chalk. These bacteria could cause illness and in the case of small babies, death. Sterilise dubious talcum in a 150°C (300°F) oven for 1 hour, stirring often.

Tincture of Benzoin: An alcoholic tincture made from resin extracted from the bar of Styrax benzoin. The tincture may be used to preserve creams, lotions and ointments. As it is antibacterial, antiseptic and antifungal it may also be used as a topical application for eczema, blackheads, boils, pimples and itching.

Note: When buying the tincture from a pharmacy be sure to specify Simple Tincture of Benzoin. Compound tincture (also known as Friar's Balsam) has other additives which may be harmful if used incorrectly.

Unguent: Another word for ointment.

Water: Water is a good medium for the growth of bacteria and, as water is often the largest proportion of any of the recipes in this book, it's necessary to use purified or distilled water to ensure that the preparations last as long as possible.

A piece of cotton wool squeezed out in cold water and patted on will set make-up and help it last longer.

Witch Hazel (Hamamelis virginiana): Distilled witch hazel extract. In this book you will find many uses for witch hazel extract — particularly for toners and astringents. Witch hazel extract is astringent, styptic and cleansing. It helps to reduce skin inflammation, the pain of stings, dandruff, bruises and swellings. Because of it's astringency it is a most useful toner for oily skin and is a reasonably good deodorant for both underarm and vaginal areas. Distilled witch hazel extract is readily available from pharmacies.

Woolfat: See Lanolin.

FURTHER READING

The Twelve Healers, E. Bach (Daniel & Co Ltd, 1964)

Aromatherapy, Robert Tisserand (Granada, 1977)

The Practice of Aromatherapy, Jean Valnet, MD (Healing Arts Press, 1980)

Martindale Pharmacopoeia, (Pharmaceutical Press, 1982)

Cosmetic & Fragrance Book, Elizabeth Franke (Simon & Schuster, 1988)

Herbs and Aromatherapy, Joannah Metcalf (Webb & Bower, 1989)

Magical Aromatherapy, Scott Cunningham (Llewellyn Publications, 1989)

Herbcraft, Nerys Purchon (Hodder & Stoughton, 1990)

The Fragrant Pharmacy, Valerie Ann Worwood (Bantam Books, 1991)

The Complete Home Guide to Aromatherapy, Erich Keller (Munchen, 1991)

The Encyclopaedia of Essential Oils, Julia Lawless (Element Books, 1992)

Aromatherapy for Scentual Awareness, Judith White and Karen Day (Nacson & Sons, 1992)

Aromatherapy, Denise Brown (Hodder & Stoughton, 1993)

Bodycraft, Nerys Purchon (Hodder & Stoughton, 1993)

INDEX